and

‖‖‖‖‖‖‖‖‖‖‖‖‖‖‖‖‖
M000306567

LIONEL® TRAINS
1901-1942 & 1945-1992

By Bruce C. Greenberg, Ph.D

**With the assistance of
Paul Ambrose, W. Stephen Bachman, and
Mike Solly**

Copyright © 1991
Greenberg Publishing Company, Inc.
7566 Main Street
Sykesville, MD 21784
(301) 795-7447

Manufactured in the United States of America

Greenberg Publishing Company, Inc. publishes the world's largest selection of Lionel, American Flyer, LGB, Marx, Ives, and other toy train publications as well as a selection of books on model and prototype railroading, dollhouse building, and collectible toys. For a complete listing of current Greenberg publications, please call 1-800-533-6644 or write to Kalmbach Publishing, 21027 Crossroads Circle, Waukesha, Wisconsin 53187.

Greenberg Shows, Inc. sponsors *Greenberg's Great Train, Dollhouse and Toy Shows*, the world's largest of its kind. The shows feature extravagant operating train layouts, and a display of magnificent dollhouses. The shows also present a huge marketplace of model and toy trains, for HO, N, and Z Scales; Lionel O and Standard Gauges; and S and 1 Gauges; plus layout accessories and railroadiana. They also offer a large selection of dollhouse miniatures and building materials, and collectible toys. Shows are scheduled along the East Coast each year from Massachusetts to Florida. For a list of our current shows please call (301) 795-7447 or write to Greenberg Publishing Company, Inc., 7566 Main Street, Sykesville, Maryland 21784 and request a show brochure.

Greenberg Auctions, a division of Greenberg Shows, Inc., offers nationally advertised auctions of toy trains and toys. Please contact our auction manager at (301) 795-7447 for further information.

ISBN: 0-89778-219-4

INTRODUCTION

This **Pocket Guide** lists all major Lionel items by number only, for the years 1901-1942 and 1945-1992 (there was no Lionel production during World War II). (NOTE: We have included the 1992 items as announced by the Lionel Corporation as of August 28, 1991. Since this is a preliminary list, these 1992 items are subject to change. Many pieces are dated 1990-91 because they were announced in 1990, but not scheduled for production until 1991.) The price quoted is for the most common variety of each item. Some varieties are worth considerably more, and some rare varieties are cited. For additional information, please consult the comprehensive guides: *Greenberg's Guide to Lionel Trains: 1901-1942, Volumes I* and *II*; *Greenberg's Guide to Lionel Trains: 1945-1969, Volumes I* and *II*; *Greenberg's Guide to Lionel Trains: 1970-1991, Volumes I* and *II*; and *Greenberg's Guide to Lionel Paper and Collectibles*, all of which are described on the rear cover.

Dates cited are catalogued dates. If there is no catalogue date, production dates are listed if known.

Lionel trains are frequently marked with "Built" or "New" dates. These dates often reflect the dates that the artist picked up from prototype photographs or the date when the artist prepared his drawings. These dates may or may not have any relation to catalogue or production dates.

We have provided five columns for each item. The first two columns give the current market values for Good, Excellent, or Like New. The "Color" column is for recording the color or other distinguishing characteristics. The "Cond" column is for recording the condition of the piece. The "$" column is for recording your cost.

Values in the **Pocket Guide** are based on prices obtained at large train meets during the summer of 1991 and on prices obtained from private transactions reported by our review panel. Prices may vary depending on your geographical location.

If you have trains to sell and you sell them to a person planning to resell them, you will NOT obtain the prices reported in this book. Rather you may expect to receive about 50 percent of these prices. For your item to be of interest to such a buyer, he must buy it for considerably less than the price listed here.

Our studies of train prices indicate that mail order prices and store prices are generally higher than those obtained at train meets. This is quite appropriate given the costs and efforts of either running a retail establishment and/or producing and distributing a price list and packing and shipping trains.

NOTES TO BUYERS

WE STRONGLY RECOMMEND THAT NOVICES DO NOT MAKE MAJOR PURCHASES WITHOUT THE ASSISTANCE OF FRIENDS WHO HAVE EXPERIENCE IN BUYING AND SELLING TRAINS.

Furthermore, extreme care should be exercised in the purchase of original prewar items which have been reproduced. Even though most reproductions are originally marked, in some cases, it has been reported that these markings have been removed.

The same care needs to be exercised in the purchase of premium priced diesels. Nearly every rare diesel cab has been reproduced from an unpainted or commonly painted shell. For further information, consult *Greenberg's Guide to Lionel Trains: 1945-1969, Volumes I* and *II*.

This **Pocket Guide** involved the collaboration of many people who generously gave their time and knowledge. Only through such cooperative ventures can studies of this kind be carried out. It is impossible for one person to put together what the factory and the marketplace dispersed to the four corners of the country (or more properly to the basements and attics of enthusiasts throughout America). I can only express my deep appreciation to my fellow enthusiasts for their dedication to toy train research. This work is not finished. Fortunately, there is always more to be learned.

Bruce C. Greenberg

TABLE OF CONTENTS

This handy reference is divided into five major sections: Prewar, Postwar, 1970-1992, Large Scale, and Collectibles and Paper. In the first three sections, production is listed numerically, using the item's catalogue number. In the Prewar section, equipment is also described by Gauge — either Standard, O, OO, or 2-⅞. The Gauge type is within the parentheses. To help you use this Guide, the edges of the pages are edged in black to correspond with each of the five sections.

If you cannot find an item or believe an item has been erroneously described or priced, please let us know. We are always glad to receive corrections or additions.

DEFINITIONS

This **Pocket Guide** lists prices for Prewar and Postwar Trains and Paper as GOOD and EXCELLENT; Collectibles are priced EXCELLENT and NEW; the prices shown for 1970-1992 and Large Scale Trains are for EXCELLENT and LIKE NEW. Prices for restored pieces fall between Good and Excellent depending on the item. Mint pieces bring a substantial premium over Excellent pieces. Fair pieces bring substantially less than Good and Excellent pieces.

In the toy train field there is a great deal of concern with exterior appearance and less concern with operation. If operation is important to you, you should ask the seller if the train runs. If the seller indicates that he does not know whether the equipment operates, you should test it. Most train meets provide test tracks for this purpose.

Trains and related items are usually classified by condition. They are defined as follows:

- **FAIR** — well-scratched, chipped, dented, rusted, or warped.
- **GOOD** — scratched, dirty, with small dents.
- **VERY GOOD** — few scratches, no dents or rust, exceptionally clean.
- **EXCELLENT** — minute scratches or nicks, no dents or rust.
- **LIKE NEW** — between Excellent and Mint; only faint signs of handling with vibrant colors; price includes original box.
- **MINT** — brand new, absolutely unmarred, unused, and in original box.
- **NEW** — refers to Lionel collectibles described in Section 5. Items are complete and unused; they may have the stamp of the store where purchased.
- **RESTORED** — we define as professionally refinished with a color that approximates the original finish. Trim and ornamentation are present and in Like New condition. The finish appears in Like New condition.

- **CP** (Current Production) — means that the item is now being manufactured or is currently available from retail stores.
- **REPRODUCTION** — is a product intended to closely resemble the original item. It may or may not be marked as such, but should be so marked. Reproductions are currently available for many desirable items.
- **NRS** (No Recorded Sales) — means that we do not know the market value of the item. The item may be very scarce and bring a substantial premium over items in its general class or it may be relatively common but unnoticed. Usually NRS listings occur when an item is first reported, although we are still discovering relatively common variations that have not been previously reported. If you have information about the value of an NRS item, please write to us.
- **(#)** — Numbers that have been put in parentheses by us do not appear on the items.
- **No Number** — means the item may have lettering but lacks an item number.
- **(no letters)** — means the item has no lettering or number on the car.

SECTION I
PREWAR

		Good	Exc	Color	Cond	$
01	Steam 4-6-4 (OO), 1938-42	120	275			
	Bild-A-Motor, 1928-31	60	150			
	Trolley, 1906-08 (Standard), 1910*	900	2300			
02	Steam 4-6-4 (OO), 1939-42	100	250			
2	Bild-A-Motor, 1928-31	60	150			
2	Countershafting, 1904-11	NRS	NRS			
2	Trolley (Standard), 1906, 1908-16*	900	2300			
03	Steam 4-6-4 (OO), 1939-42	120	300			
3	Trolley (Standard), 1906-13	1400	3450			
04	Steam 4-6-4 (OO), 1939-42	110	275			
4	Electric 0-4-0 (O), 1928-32*	450	800			
4	Trolley (Standard), 1906-12	3000	5750			
4U	#4 Kit form (O), 1928-29	800	1250			
5	Electric (2-7/8") (see 100)					
5	Steam 0-4-0 (Standard), 1906-26	800	1375			
6	Steam 4-4-0 (Standard), 1906-23	800	1375			
7	Steam 4-4-0 (Standard), 1910-23*	1800	3200			
8	Electric 0-4-0 (Standard), 1925-32	90	175			
8	Trolley (Standard), 1908-09*	3000	5750			
8E	Electric 0-4-0 (Standard)	95	180			
9	Electric 0-4-0 (Standard), 1929*	1200	2300			
9	Trolley (Standard), 1909	3000	5750			
9E	Electric 0-4-0 (Std.), 1928-30*	600	1375			
9U	Electric 0-4-0 (Std.), 1928-29	700	1550			
10	Electric 0-4-0 (Standard), 1925-29	90	195			
10	Interurban (Standard), 1910-12	800	1700			
10E	Electric 0-4-0 (Standard), 26-36	95	200			
011	Switches, pair (O), 1933-37	20	50			
11	Flatcar (Standard), 1906-26	32	60			
012	Switches, pair (O), 1927-33	12	35			
12	Gondola (Standard), 1906-26	32	60			
013	012 Switches (2), 439 Panel Board	55	150			
13	Cattle Car (Standard), 1906-26	50	95			
0014	Boxcar (OO), 1938-42	25	60			
14	Boxcar (Standard), 1906-26	50	95			
0015	Tank Car (OO), 1938-42	25	60			
15	Oil Car (Standard), 1906-26	35	60			
0016	Hopper Car (OO), 1938-42	35	80			
16	Ballast Dump Car (Std.), 1906-26	85	200			
0017	Caboose (OO), 1938-42	25	60			
17	Caboose (Standard), 1906-26	35	60			
18	Pullman (Standard), 1906-27	90	160			
19	Combine (Standard), 1906-26	90	160			
020	90° Crossover (O), 1915-42	2	6			

Prewar		Good	Exc	Color	Cond	$
020X	45° Crossover (O), 1917-42	3	8	___	___	___
20	90° Crossover (Standard)	2	6	___	___	___
20	Direct Current Reducer, 1906	NRS	NRS	___	___	___
20X	45° Crossover (Standard), 1928-32	3	8	___	___	___
021	Switches, pair (O), 1915-37	8	25	___	___	___
21	Switches, pair (Standard), 1915-25	10	25	___	___	___
21	90° Crossover (Standard), 1906	7	18	___	___	___
022	Switches, pair, Rem. (O), 1938-42	25	60	___	___	___
22	Switches, pair (Standard), 1906-25	10	30	___	___	___
023	Bumper (O), 1915-33	5	15	___	___	___
23	Bumper (Standard), 1906-23	5	15	___	___	___
0024	P R R Boxcar (OO), 1939-42	25	60	___	___	___
24	Railway Station (Standard), 1906	NRS	NRS	___	___	___
025	Bumper (O), 1928-42	5	15	___	___	___
0025	Tank Car (OO), 1939-42	25	60	___	___	___
25	Open Station, 1906	NRS	NRS	___	___	___
25	Bumper (Standard), 1927-42	7	20	___	___	___
0027	Caboose (OO), 1939-42	25	60	___	___	___
26	Passenger Bridge, 1906	NRS	NRS	___	___	___
27	Lighting Set, 1911-23	7	20	___	___	___
27	Station (Standard), 1909-12	NRS	NRS	___	___	___
28	Double Station w/dome, 1909-12	NRS	NRS	___	___	___
29	Day Coach (Standard), 1909-27	375	700	___	___	___
31	Combine (Standard), 1921-25	55	95	___	___	___
32	Mail Car (Standard), 1921-25	70	115	___	___	___
32	Miniature Figures, 1909-18	—	85	___	___	___
33	Electric 0-6-0, Early (Std.), 1912	250	700	___	___	___
33	Electric 0-4-0, Later (Std.), 1913-24	90	160	___	___	___
34	Electric 0-6-0 (Standard), 1912	450	1025	___	___	___
34	Electric 0-4-0 (Standard), 1913	175	450	___	___	___
35	Blvd. Lamp, 6-1/8" high, 1940-42	10	30	___	___	___
35	Pullman, first series (Std.), 1912-13	80	115	___	___	___
35	Pullman, second series (Standard)	30	60	___	___	___
35	Pullman, third series (Standard)	30	45	___	___	___
36	Observation, first series (Standard)	80	115	___	___	___
36	Observation, second series (Std.)	30	60	___	___	___
36	Observation, third series (Standard)	30	45	___	___	___
38	Electric 0-4-0 (Standard), 1913-24	70	140	___	___	___
41	Accessory Contactor, 1937-42	1	3	___	___	___
042	Switches, pair (O), 1938-42	15	35	___	___	___
42	Electric 0-4-4-0, square hood (Standard), 1912	900	1700	___	___	___
42	Electric 0-4-4-0, round hood (Standard), 1913-23	225	550	___	___	___
043/43	Bild-A-Motor Gear Set, 29	NRS	NRS	___	___	___
43	Boat, Runabout, 1933-36, 1939-41	250	400	___	___	___
0044	Boxcar (OO), 1939-42	25	60	___	___	___
0044K	Boxcar Kit (OO), 1939-42	50	120	___	___	___

		Good	Exc	Color	Cond	$
44	Boat, Speedster, 1935-36	300	525			
45/045/45N	Auto. Gateman, 1935-42	15	35			
0045	Tank Car (OO), 1939-42	25	60			
0045K	Tank Car Kit (OO), 1939-42	50	120			
0046	Hopper Car (OO), 1939-42	25	60			
0046K	Hopper Car Kit (OO), 1939-42	40	90			
46	Crossing Gate, 1939-42	30	90			
0047	Caboose (OO), 1939-42	25	60			
0047K	Caboose, Kit (OO), 1939-42	50	120			
47	Crossing Gate, 1939-42	35	115			
48W	Whistle Station, 1937-42	20	40			
49	Lionel Airport, 1937-39	70	210			
50	Airplane, 1936	60	180			
50	Electric 0-4-0 (Standard), 1924	100	170			
50	Cardboard Train, Cars, Accessory (O), 1943*	200	350			
51	Steam 0-4-0, 5 Late, eight-wheel tender (Standard)	750	1150			
51	Lionel Airport, 1936, 1938	70	210			
52	Lamp Post, 1933-41	30	75			
53	Elec. 0-4-4-0, Early (Std.), 12-14	800	1950			
53	Electric 0-4-0, Later (Standard)	450	925			
53	Elec. 0-4-0, Latest (Std.), 1920-21	150	350			
53	Lamp Post, 1931-42	20	40			
54	Elec. 0-4-4-0, Early (Std.), 1912*	2500	4000			
54	Elec. 0-4-4-0, Late (Std.), 13-23	1500	2750			
54	Lamp Post, 1929-35	30	40			
55	Airplane with stand, 1937-39	150	425			
56	Lamp Post, removable lens and cap, 1924-42	20	35			
57	Lamp Post, w/street names, 1922-42	30	50			
58	Lamp Post, 7-3/8" high, 1922-42	20	40			
59	Lamp Post, 8-3/4" high, 1920-36	25	50			
60/060	Telegraph Post (Standard O)	2	7			
60	Electric 0-4-0, F. A. O. S. (Std.)	—	2300			
61	Electric 0-4-4-0, F. A. O. S. (Std.)	—	2750			
61	Lamp Post, one globe, 1914-36	35	60			
62	Electric 0-4-0, F. A. O. S. (Std.)	—	2300			
62	Semaphore, 1920-32	10	30			
63	Lamp Post, two globes, 1933-42	100	180			
63	Semaphore, 1915-21	10	30			
64	Lamp Post, 1940-42	10	40			
64	Semaphore, 6-3/4" high, 1915-21	12	45			
65	Semaphore, one-arm, 1915-26	11	35			
65	Whistle, 1935 only	2	4			
66	Semaphore, two-arm, 1915-26	11	35			
66	Whistle Controller, 1936-39	2	4			
67	Lamp Post, 1915-32	45	90			

Prewar		Good	Exc	Color	Cond	$
67	Whistle Controller, 1936-39	2	4			
68/068	Crossing Sign	3	6			
69/069/69N	Elec. Warning Signal, 21-42	11	30			
70	Outfit: (2) 62s, (1) 59, (1) 68	50	120			
071	(6) 060 Telegraph Poles (O), 24-42	50	120			
71	(6) 60 Telegraph Poles (Standard)	50	120			
0072	Switches, pair (OO), 1938-42	120	200			
0074	Boxcar (OO), 1939-42	25	60			
0075	Tank Car (OO), 1939-42	25	60			
076/76	Block Signal, 1923-28	15	50			
76	Warning Bell and Shack, 1939-42	60	175			
0077	Caboose (OO), 1939-42	25	60			
77/077/77N	Auto. Crossing Gate, 23-39	15	35			
78/078	Train Signal (Standard), 24-32	20	60			
79	Flashing Signal, 1928-40	30	70			
80/080/80N	Semaphore (Std.), 26-42	35	80			
80	Automobile, 1912-16	600	1300			
81	Automobile, 1912-16	600	1300			
81	Controlling Rheostat, 1927-33	1	4			
81	Crossing Signal, 1927-33	1	4			
82/082/82N	Semaphore, 1927-42	45	90			
83	Flashing Traffic Signal, 1927-42	35	85			
084	Semaphore, 1928-32	40	85			
84	Semaphore, 1927-32	40	85			
84	(2) Automobiles	1300	3000			
85	Telegraph Pole (Standard), 1929-42	4	12			
85	(2) Automobiles	1200	3000			
86	(6) Telegraph Poles, 1929-42	45	120			
87	Flashing Crossing Signal, 1927-42	35	90			
88	Battery Rheostat, 1915-27	1	4			
88	Rheostat Controller, 1933-42	1	4			
89	Flag Pole, 1923-34	8	25			
90	Flag Pole, 1927-42	15	40			
91	Circuit Breaker, 1930-42	7	20			
092	Signal Tower, 1923-27	40	100			
92	Floodlight Tower, 1931-42*	70	180			
93	Water Tower, 1931-42	15	35			
94	High Tension Tower, 1932-42*	70	175			
95	Controlling Rheostat, 1934-42	1	4			
96	Coal Elevator, manual, 1938-40	70	180			
097	Telegraph Set (O)	35	70			
97	Coal Elevator, 1938-42	70	180			
98	Coal Bunker, 1938-40	150	350			
99/099/99N	Train Control, 1932-42	30	90			
100	Electric Locomotive (2-7/8")*	3000	4600			
100	Trolley, 1910, 1912-15	700	1700			
100	(2) Bridge Appro. (Std.), 1920-31	10	25			
100	Wooden Gondola (2-7/8"), 1901	NRS	NRS			

		Good	Exc	Color	Cond	$
101	Bridge Span, (2) Approaches (Standard), 1920-31	15	50			
101	Summer Trolley (Std.), 1910	800	2150			
102	(2) Bridge Spans, (2) Approaches (Standard), 1920-31	25	70			
103	Bridge (Standard), 1913-16	10	30			
103	(3) Bridge Spans, (2) Approaches (Standard), 1920-31	45	120			
104	Bridge Span (Standard), 1920-31	10	30			
104	Tunnel (Standard), 1909-14	30	100			
105	Bridge (Standard), 1911-14	10	30			
105	(2) Bridge Approaches (O), 1920-31	5	15			
106	Bridge Span, (2) Appro. (O), 20-31	20	60			
107	DC reducer, 110 V, 1923-32	NRS	NRS			
108	(2) Bridge Spans, (2) Approaches (O), 1920-31	20	60			
109	(3) Bridge Spans, (2) Approaches (O), 1920-32	25	70			
109	Tunnel (Standard), 1913-14	17	40			
110	Bridge Span (O), 1920-31	5	15			
111	Box of 50 Bulbs, 1920-31	—	120			
112	Gondola (Standard), 1910-26	25	45			
112	Station, 1931-35	80	200			
113	Cattle Car (Standard), 1912-26	35	60			
113	Station, 1931-34	100	230			
114	Boxcar (Standard), 1912-26	35	60			
114	Station, 1931-34	450	1200			
115	Station, 1935-42*	125	270			
116	Station, 1935-42*	450	1200			
116	Ballast Car (Standard), 1910-26	40	70			
117	Caboose (Standard), 1912-26	30	60			
117	Station, 1936-42	75	180			
118	Tunnel, 8" long (O), 1922-32	7	20			
118L	Tunnel, 8" long, 1927	9	25			
119	Tunnel, 12" long, 1920-42	7	20			
119L	Tunnel, 12" long, 1927-33	9	25			
120	Tunnel, 17" long, 1922-27	18	40			
120L	Tunnel, 1927-42	25	50			
121	Station (Standard), 1909-16	80	240			
121	Station (Standard), 1920-26	45	120			
121X	Station (Standard), 1917-19	80	240			
122	Station (Standard), 1920-30	45	120			
123	Station (Standard), 1920-23	45	120			
123	Tunnel, 18-1/2" long (O), 1933-42	50	120			
124	Station, "Lionel City", 1920-36*	45	120			
125	Station, "Lionelville", 1923-25	50	120			
125	Track Template, 1938	1	4			
126	Station, "Lionelville", 1923-36	50	120			

		Good	Exc	Color	Cond	$
127	Station, "Lionel Town", 1923-36	35	90			
128	124 Station and Terrace, 28-35*	500	1300			
128	115 Station and Terrace, 36-42*	500	1300			
129	Terrace, 1928-42*	450	1015			
130	Tunnel, 26" long, 1920-36	120	300			
130L	Tunnel, 26" long, 1927-33	120	300			
131	Corner Display, 1924-28	70	250			
132	Corner Grass Plot, 1924-28	70	250			
133	Heart Shaped Plot, 1924-28	70	250			
134	Oval Shaped Plot, 1924-28	70	250			
134	Sta., "Lionel City", w/stop, 37-42	140	300			
135	Circular Plot, 1924-28	70	250			
136	Large Elevation, 1924-28	NRS	NRS			
136	Sta., "Lionelville", w/stop, 37-42	60	120			
137	Station, with stop, 1937-42	60	120			
140L	Tunnel, 37" long, 1927-32	190	425			
150	Electric 0-4-0, Early (O), 1917	65	100			
150	Electric 0-4-0, Late (O), 1918-25	65	100			
152	Electric 0-4-0 (O), 1917-27	70	115			
152	Crossing Gate, 1940-42	9	25			
153	Block Signal, 1940-42	10	30			
153	Electric 0-4-0 (O), 1924-25	75	140			
154	Electric 0-4-0 (O), 1917-23	75	160			
154	Highway Signal, 1940-42	10	30			
155	Freight Shed, 1930-42*	120	240			
156	Electric 4-4-4 (O), 1917-23	450	800			
156	Electric 0-4-0 (O), 1917-23	450	800			
156	Station Platform, 1939-42	20	65			
156X	Electric 0-4-0 (O), 1923-24	325	500			
157	Hand Truck, 1930-32	15	35			
158	Electric 0-4-0 (O), 1923-24	60	115			
158	(2) 156s and (1) 136, 1940-42	75	180			
159	Block Actuator, 1940	10	30			
161	Baggage Truck, 1930-32*	20	60			
162	Dump Truck, 1930-32*	22	60			
163	(2) 157 Hand Trucks, one 162 Dump, and one 161 Baggage, boxed, 30-42*	90	250			
164	Log Loader, 1940-42	70	180			
165	Magnetic Crane, 1940-42	70	180			
166	Whistle Controller, 1940-42	2	4			
167	Whistle Controller, 1940-42	2	4			
167X	Whistle Controller (OO), 1940-42	2	5			
169	Controller, 1940-42	1	4			
170	DC reducer, 220 volts, 1914-38	2	5			
171	DC to AC Inverter, 110 volts, 36-42	2	5			
172	DC to AC Inverter, 229 volts, 39-42	2	5			
180	Pullman (Standard), 1911-21	90	115			
181	Combine (Standard), 1911-21	90	150			

		Good	Exc	Color	Cond	$
182	Observation (Standard), 1911-21	90	140			
184	Bungalow, illuminated, 1923-32*	40	70			
185	Bungalow, 1923-24	30	55			
186	(5) 184 Bungalows, 1923-32	200	425			
186	Log Loader Outfit, 1940-41	100	250			
187	(5) 185 Bungalows, boxed, 23-24	125	300			
188	Elevator and Car Set, 1938-41	90	240			
189	Villa, illuminated, 1923-32*	75	180			
190	Observation (Std.), 1914-18, 23-27	90	150			
191	Villa, illuminated, 1923-32*	75	170			
192	Illuminated Villa Set: 191 Villa, 189					
	Villa, two 184 Bungalows, 1927-32	NRS	NRS			
193	Accessory Set, 1927-29	140	350			
194	Accessory Set, 1927-29	140	350			
195	Terrace, 1927-30	275	725			
196	Accessory Set, 1927	150	350			
200	Electric Express (2-7/8"), 1903*	4000	6000			
200	Turntable, 1928-33*	75	180			
200	Wooden Gondola (2-7/8"), 1902	NRS	NRS			
200	Trailer, matches #2 Trolley (Std.)	—	3600			
201	Steam 0-6-0 (O), 1940-42	325	700			
202	Summer Trolley, 1910-13	800	2850			
203	Armored Loco 0-4-0 (O), 17-21	700	2400			
203	Steam 0-6-0 (O), 1940-42	275	480			
204	Steam 2-4-2 (O), 1940	30	75			
205	Merchandise Containers, 1930-38*					
	set of three	120	300			
206	Sack of Coal, 1938-42	5	18			
208	Tool Set, 1934-42*	30	90			
0209	Barrels, 1934-42	4	12			
209	Wooden Barrels, 1934-42	6	18			
210	Switches, pair (Std.), 1926, 34-42	10	30			
211	Flatcar (Standard), 1926-40*	60	90			
212	Gondola (Standard), 1926-40*	75	115			
213	Cattle Car (Standard), 1926-40*	150	230			
214	Boxcar (Standard), 1926-40*	175	315			
214R	Refrig. Car (Std.), 1929-40*	450	800			
215	Tank Car (Standard), 1926-40*	150	200			
216	Hopper Car (Standard), 1926-38*	175	285			
217	Caboose (Standard), 1926-40*	120	170			
217	Lighting Set, 1914-23	NRS	NRS			
218	Dump Car (Standard), 1926-38*	175	275			
219	Crane (Standard), 1926-40*	120	200			
220	Floodlight Car (Std.), 1931-40*	200	315			
220	Switches, pair (Standard), 1926*	10	30			
222	Switches, pair (Standard), 1926-32	20	50			
223	Switches, pair (Standard), 1932-42	30	80			
224/224E	Steam 2-6-2 (O), 1938-42	75	170			

225 E

300 35⁰

		Good	Exc	Color	Cond	$
225	222 Switches & 439 Panel, 29-32	75	175			
225/225E • Steam 2-6-2 (O), 1938-42		200	345			
226/226E Steam 2-6-4 (O), 1938-41		400	750			
227	Steam Switcher 0-6-0 (O), 39-42	800	1250			
228	Steam Switcher 0-6-0 (O), 39-42	800	1250			
229	Steam 2-4-2 (O), 1939-42	50	85			
230	Steam Switcher 0-6-0 (O), 39-42	900	1725			
231	Steam Switcher 0-6-0 (O), 1939	900	1725			
232	Steam Switcher 0-6-0 (O), 1930	900	1725			
233	Steam Switcher 0-6-0 (O), 40-42	900	1725			
238/238E Steam 4-4-2 (O), 1936-38		175	285			
248	Electric 0-4-0 (O), 1926-32	75	140			
249/249E Steam 2-4-2 (O), 1936-37		125	200			
250E Hiawatha, Steam 0-4-0 (O), 1935-42*		800	1495			
250	Electric 0-4-0, Early (O), 1926	150	230			
250	Electric 0-4-0, Late (O), 1934	150	230			
251	Electric 0-4-0 (O), 1925-32	175	285			
251E	Electric 0-4-0 (O), 1927-32	175	285			
252	Electric 0-4-0 (O), 1926-32	85	140			
252E	Electric 0-4-0 (O), 1933-35	95	150			
253	Electric 0-4-0 (O), 1924-32	80	140			
253E	Electric 0-4-0 (O), 1931-36	100	170			
254	Electric 0-4-0 (O), 1924-32	100	200			
254E	Electric 0-4-0 (O), 1927-34	120	230			
255E	Steam 2-4-2 (O), 1935-36	375	575			
256	Electric 0-4-4-0 (O), 1924-30*	400	630			
257	Steam 0-4-0 (O), 1930	90	200			
258	Steam 2-4-0, Early (O), 1930	80	175			
258	Steam 2-4-2, Late (O), 1941	35	60			
259	Steam 2-4-2 (O), 1932	55	90			
259E	Steam 2-4-2 (O), 33-34, 36-38	45	70			
260E	Steam 2-4-2 (O), 1930-35*	375	515			
261	Steam 2-4-2 (O), 1931	140	230			
261E	Steam 2-4-2 (O), 1935	160	255			
262	Steam 2-4-2 (O), 1931-32	100	190			
262E	Steam 2-4-2 (O), 1933-34	110	200			
263E	Steam 2-4-2 (O), 1936-39*	375	630			
264E	Steam 2-4-2 (O), 1935-36	110	260			
265E	Steam 2-4-2 (O), 1935-39	130	225			
270	Bridge, 10" long (O), 1931-42	12	25			
270	Lighting Set, 1915-23	NRS	NRS			
271	(2) 270 Spans (O), 31-33, 35-40	25	70			
271	Lighting Set, 1915-23	NRS	NRS			
272	(3) 270 Spans (O), 1931-33, 35-40	25	70			
280	Bridge, 14" long (Std.), 1931-42	25	50			
281	(2) Bridge Spans (Standard), 1931-33, 35-40	50	95			

		Good	Exc	Color	Cond	$
282	(3) Bridge Spans (Standard), 1931-33, 35-40	75	145	___	___	___
289E	Steam 2-4-2 (O), 1937	150	260	___	___	___
300	Electric Trolley Car (2-7/8"), 1903-05	2000	3600	___	___	___
300	Hell Gate Bridge (Std.), 1928-42*	400	1100	___	___	___
301	Batteries (2-7/8"), 1903-05	NRS	NRS	___	___	___
303	Summer Trolley (2-7/8")	1500	3600	___	___	___
308	(5) Signs (O), 1940-42	6	18	___	___	___
309	Electric Trolley Trailer (2-7/8"), 1904-05	1700	2650	___	___	___
309	Pullman (Standard), 1924-39	90	170	___	___	___
310	Baggage (Standard), 1924-39	90	170	___	___	___
310	Rails and Ties, complete section (2-7/8"), 1903-05	NRS	NRS	___	___	___
312	Observation (Standard), 1924-39	90	170	___	___	___
313	Bascule Bridge (O), 1940-42	175	450	___	___	___
314	Girder Bridge (O), 1940-42	6	20	___	___	___
315	Trestle Bridge (O), 1940-42	20	50	___	___	___
316	Trestle Bridge (O), 1940-42	10	35	___	___	___
318	Electric 0-4-0 (Std.), 1924-32	150	285	___	___	___
318E	Electric 0-4-0 (Std.), 1926-35	150	285	___	___	___
319	Pullman (Standard), 1924-27	100	140	___	___	___
320	Baggage (Standard), 1925-27	125	170	___	___	___
320	Turnout (2-7/8"), 1903-05	NRS	NRS	___	___	___
322	Observation (Standard), 1924-27	90	140	___	___	___
330	Crossing, 90° (2-7/8"), 1903-05	NRS	NRS	___	___	___
332	Baggage (Standard), 1929	45	85	___	___	___
337	Pullman (Standard), 1925-32	45	85	___	___	___
338	Observation (Standard)	45	85	___	___	___
339	Pullman (Standard), 1925-33	45	85	___	___	___
340	Suspension Bridge (2-7/8"), 1903-05	NRS	NRS	___	___	___
341	Observation (Standard), 1925-33	45	85	___	___	___
350	Track Bumper (2-7/8"), 1903-05	20	40	___	___	___
370	Jars and Plates (2-7/8"), 1903-05	NRS	NRS	___	___	___
380	Electric 0-4-0 (Std.), 1923-27	200	400	___	___	___
380	Elevated Pillars (2-7/8"), 1903-05	40	90	___	___	___
380E	Electric 0-4-0 (Std.), 1926-28	200	400	___	___	___
381	Electric 4-4-4 (Std.), 1928-29*	1500	4200	___	___	___
381E	Electric 4-4-4 (Std.), 1928-36*	1200	3000	___	___	___
381U	Electric 4-4-4 (Std.), 1928-29*	1600	4550	___	___	___
384	Steam 2-4-0 (Std.), 1930-32*	350	515	___	___	___
384E	Steam 2-4-0 (Std.), 1930-32*	350	515	___	___	___
385E	Steam 2-4-2 (Std.), 1933-39*	450	775	___	___	___
390	Steam 2-4-2 (Standard), 1929*	450	860	___	___	___
390E	Steam 2-4-2 (Std.), 1929-31*	450	750	___	___	___
392E	Steam 4-4-2 (Std.), 1932-39*	850	1375	___	___	___

		Good	Exc	Color	Cond	$
400	Express Trail Car (2-7/8"), 1903	2000	3600			
400E	Steam 4-4-4 (Std.), 1931-40*	1200	2300			
402	Electric 0-4-4-0 (Std.), 1923-27	425	575			
402E	Electric 0-4-4-0 (Std.), 26-29	425	575			
408E	Electric 0-4-4-0 (Std.), 27-36*	600	1375			
412	Pull., "California" (Std.), 29-35*	850	1800			
413	Pull., "Colorado" (Std.), 29-35*	850	1800			
414	Pull., "Illinois" (Std.), 1929-35*	975	2500			
416	Obs., "New York" (Std.), 29-35*	850	1800			
418	Pullman (Standard), 1923-32*	175	280			
419	Combination (Std.), 1923-32*	175	280			
420	Pullman, "Faye" (Std.), 1930-40*	525	1000			
421	Pull., "Westphal" (Std.) 1930-40*	525	1000			
422	Obs., "Tempel" (Std.), 1930-40*	525	1000			
424	Pullman "Liberty Belle" (Standard), 1931-40*	350	600			
425	Pullman "Stephen Girard" (Standard), 1931-40*	350	600			
426	Obs. "Coral Isle" (Std.), 1931-40*	350	600			
428	Pullman (Standard), 1926-30*	300	345			
429	Combine (Standard), 1926-30*	300	345			
430	Observation (Standard), 1926-30*	300	345			
431	Diner (Standard), 1927-32*	350	550			
435	Power Station, 1926-38*	75	180			
436	Power Station, 1926-37*	100	180			
437	Switch/Signal Tower, 1926-37*	175	350			
438	Signal Tower, 1927-39*	140	350			
439	Panel Board, 1928-42*	50	125			
440/0440/440N	Signal Bridge, 32-42*	150	600			
440C	Panel Board, 1932-42	35	90			
441	Weighing Station (Std.), 1932-36	400	850			
442	Landscape Diner, 1938-42	60	180			
444	Roundhouse (Standard), 32-35*	1100	3000			
444-18	Roundhouse Clip, 1933	NRS	NRS			
450	Macy's, Electric 0-4-0 (O), 1930	250	480			
450	Set: 450 and Matching (2) 605s, 606	750	1200			
455	Electric Range, 1930, 1932-33	200	600			
490	Observation (Standard), 1923-32*	175	285			
500	Dealer Display, 1927-28	NRS	NRS			
500	Electric Derrick Car (2-7/8"), 1903-04*	3000	4800			
501	Dealer Display, 1927-28	NRS	NRS			
502	Dealer Display, 1927-28	NRS	NRS			
503	Dealer Display, 1927-28	NRS	NRS			
504	Dealer Display, 1924-28	NRS	NRS			
505	Dealer Display, 1924-28	NRS	NRS			
506	Dealer Display, 1924-28	NRS	NRS			

		Good	Exc	Color	Cond	$
507	Dealer Display, 1924-28	NRS	NRS			
508	Dealer Display, 1924-28	NRS	NRS			
509	Dealer Display, 1924-28	NRS	NRS			
510	Dealer Display, 1927-28	NRS	NRS			
511	Flatcar (Standard), 1927-40	35	60			
512	Gondola (Standard), 1927-39	40	65			
513	Cattle Car (Standard), 1927-38	75	115			
514	Boxcar (Standard), 1929-40	100	140			
514	Refrigerator Car (Std.), 1927-28	120	170			
514R	Refrigerator Car (Std.), 1929-40	120	170			
515	Tank Car (Standard), 1927-40	100	170			
516	Hopper Car (Standard), 1928-40	125	200			
517	Caboose (Standard), 1927-40	35	75			
520	Floodlight Car (Std.), 1931-40	100	170			
529	Pullman (O), 1926-32	15	25			
530	Observation (O), 1926-32	15	25			
550	Miniature Figures (Standard), boxed, 1932-36*	110	180			
551	Engineer (Standard), 1932	15	25			
552	Conductor (Standard), 1932	15	25			
553	Porter (Standard), 1932	15	25			
554	Male Passenger (Standard), 1932	15	25			
555	Female Passenger (Standard), 1932	15	25			
556	Red Cap Figure (Standard), 1932	15	25			
600	Derrick Trailer (2-7/8"), 1903-04	3500	6000			
600	Pullman, Early (O), 1915-23	15	35			
600	Pullman, Late (O), 1933-42	35	85			
601	Observation, Late (O), 1933-42	35	85			
601	Pullman, Early (O), 1915-23	10	30			
602	Baggage, Lionel Lines (O), 33-42	40	90			
602	N Y C Baggage (O), 1915-23	15	35			
602	Observation (O), 1922, uncat.	10	25			
603	Pullman, Early (O), 1922, uncat.	30	70			
603	Pullman, Later (O), 1920-25	15	40			
603	Pullman, Latest, 1931-36	20	40			
604	Observation, Later (O), 1920-25	20	40			
604	Observation, Latest (O), 1931-36	20	40			
605	Pullman (O), 1925-32	75	145			
606	Observation (O), 1925-32	75	145			
607	Pullman (O), 1926-27	25	45			
608	Observation (O), 1926-37	25	45			
609	Pullman (O), 1937	30	70			
610	Pullman, Early (O), 1915-25	30	60			
610	Pullman, Late (O), 1926-30	30	60			
611	Observation (O), 1937	30	70			
612	Observation, Early (O), 1915-25	25	60			
612	Observation, Late (O), 1926-30	25	60			
613	Pullman (O), 1931-40*	50	115			

15

Prewar

		Good	Exc	Color	Cond	$
614	Observation (O), 1931-40*	50	115			
615	Baggage (O), 1933-40*	60	145			
616E/616W	Diesel only (O), 1935-41	50	115			
616E/616W	Set: 616, (2) 617s, 618	200	315			
617	Coach (O), 1935-41	40	85			
618	Observation (O), 1935-41	40	85			
619	Combine (O)	85	235			
620	Floodlight Car (O), 1937-42	20	30			
629	Pullman (O), 1924-32	15	30			
630	Observation, 1926-31	15	30			
636W	Diesel only (O), 1936-41	75	145			
636W	Set: 636W, (2) 637s, 638	200	460			
637	Coach (O), 1936-39	70	115			
638	Observation (O), 1936-39	50	115			
651	Flatcar (O), 1935-40	15	30			
652	Gondola (O), 1935-40	15	30			
653	Hopper Car (O), 1934-40	25	40			
654	Tank Car (O), 1934-38	15	35			
655	Boxcar (O), 1934-42	25	40			
656	Cattle Car (O), 1935-40	30	60			
657	Caboose (O), 1934-42	15	30			
659	Dump Car (O), 1935-42	30	50			
700	Electric 0-4-0 (O), 1913-16	250	460			
700	Window Display (2-7/8"), 03-05	NRS	NRS			
700E	Steam 4-6-4, Scale Hudson, "5344" (O), 1937-42*	1900	4000			
700K	Steam 4-6-4, unbuilt kit (O), 1938-42	3500	5750			
701	Electric 0-4-0 (O), 1913-16	350	575			
701	Steam 0-6-0 (see 708)					
702	Baggage (O), 1917-21	90	230			
703	Electric 4-4-4 (O), 1913-16	1300	2300			
706	Electric 0-4-0 (O), 1913-16	300	575			
708	Steam 0-6-0, "8976" on boiler front (O), 1939-42*	1900	3450			
710	Pullman (O), 1924-34	125	230			
711	R.C. Switches, pair (O72), 35-42	75	170			
712	Observation (O), 1924-34	125	230			
714	Boxcar, scale (O), 1940-42*	300	575			
714K	Boxcar, unbuilt kit (O), 40-42	—	925			
715	Shell Tank Car, scale (O), 40-42*	275	515			
715K	Tank Car, unbuilt kit (O), 40-42	—	745			
716	Hopper Car, scale (O), 1940-42*	400	700			
716K	Hopper, unbuilt kit (O), 40-42	—	975			
717	Caboose (O), 1940-42*	325	515			
717K	Caboose, unbuilt kit (O), 40-42	—	745			
720	90° Crossing (O72), 1935-42	7	18			
721	Manual Switches, pr. (O72), 35-42	45	120			

		Good	Exc	Color	Cond	$
730	90° Crossing (O72), 1935-42	20	40			
731	R.C. Switches, pair, T-rail (O72), 1935-42	85	200			
752E/752W	Set: 752, (2) 753s, 754 (O), 1934-41*	600	925			
752E	Set: 752, 753, 754 (O), 34-41*	400	750			
752E	Diesel only	150	260			
753	Coach (O), 1936-41	75	170			
754	Observation (O), 1936-41	75	170			
760	16-piece Curved Track (O72), 1935-42	25	60			
761	Curved Track (O72), 1934-42	1	2.50			
762	Straight Track (O72), 1934-42	1	2.50			
762	Ins. Straight Track (O72), 1934-42	2	5			
763E	Steam 4-6-4 (O), 1937-42	1000	3150			
771	Curved Track, T-rail (O72), 35-42	3	7			
772	Straight Track, T-rail (O72), 35-42	4	12			
773	Fishplate Outfit (O72), 1936-42	25	35			
782	M R Combine (O), 1935-41*	185	450			
783	M R Coach (O), 1935-41*	185	450			
784	M R Observation (O), 1935-41*	185	450			
792	Rail Chief Combine (O), 37-41*	300	925			
793	Rail Chief Coach (O), 1937-41*	300	925			
794	Rail Chief Obs. (O), 1927-41*	300	925			
800	Boxcar (O), 1915-26	10	40			
800	Boxcar (2-7/8"), 1904-05*	2000	3450			
801	Caboose (O), 1915-26	15	40			
802	Stock Car (O), 1915-26	20	45			
803	Hopper Car, Early (O), 1923-28	25	40			
803	Hopper Car, Late (O), 1929-34	20	30			
804	Tank Car (O), 1923-28	25	40			
805	Boxcar (O), 1927-34	30	45			
806	Stock Car (O), 1927-34	25	40			
807	Caboose (O), 1927-40	20	30			
809	Dump Car (O), 1930-41	25	40			
810	Crane (O), 1930-42	75	125			
811	Flatcar (O), 1926-40	40	60			
812	Gondola (O), 1926-42	20	45			
813	Stock Car (O), 1926-42	40	85			
814	Boxcar (O), 1926-42	40	85			
814R	Refrigerator Car (O), 1929-42	100	200			
815	Tank Car (O), 1926-42	35	75			
816	Hopper Car (O), 1927-42	45	100			
817	Caboose (O), 1926-42	25	70			
820	Boxcar (O), 1915-26	25	45			
820	Floodlight Car (O), 1931-42	75	140			
821	Stock Car (O), 1915-16, 1925-26	45	85			
822	Caboose (O), 1915-26	35	60			

		Good	Exc	Color	Cond	$
831	Flatcar (O), 1927-34	20	35			
840	Industrial Power Sta., 1928-40*	1200	3450			
900	Ammunition Car (O), 1917-21	100	230			
900	Box Trail Car (2-7/8"), 1904-05	2000	3450			
901	Gondola (O), 1919-27	20	40			
902	Gondola (O), 1927-34	15	30			
910	Grove of Trees, 1932-42	70	170			
911	Country Estate	175	400			
912	Suburban Home	175	400			
913	Landscaped Bungalow, 1940-42	140	315			
914	Park Landscape, 1932-35	90	230			
915	Tunnel, 1932, 1934-35	100	285			
916	Tunnel, 29-1/4" long, 1935	70	170			
917	Scenic Hillside, 1932-36	90	230			
918	Scenic Hillside, 1932-36	90	230			
919	Park Grass, bag, 1932-42	7	17			
920	Village, 1932-33	600	1725			
921	Scenic Park, 3 pieces, 1932-33	1000	2875			
921C	Park Center, 1932-33	400	1150			
922	Terrace, 1932-36	80	170			
923	Tunnel, 40-1/4" long, 1933-42	70	230			
924	Tunnel, 30" long (O72), 1935-42	50	140			
925	Lubricant, 1935-42	1	3			
927	Flag Plot, 1937-42	60	140			
1000	Coach (2-7/8"), 1905*	3500	5750			
1000	Trailer (2-7/8")	NRS	NRS			
1010	Electric 0-4-0 (O), 1931-32	45	85			
1010	Trailer, matches 10 Interurban	600	1600			
1011	Pullman (O), 1931-32	10	35			
1012	Station, 1932	20	40			
1015	Steam 0-4-0 (O), 1931-32	60	100			
1017	Winner Station, 1933	15	45			
1019	Observation (O), 1931-32	25	60			
1020	Baggage (O), 1931-32	50	115			
1021	90° Crossover (O27), 1932-42	1	3			
1022	Tunnel, 18-3/4" long (O), 1935-42	7	20			
1023	Tunnel, 19" long, 1934-42	10	20			
1024	Switches, pair (O27), 1937-42	2	15			
1025	Bumper (O27), 1940-42	6	20			
1027	Transformer in Tin Station, 1934	15	45			
1028	Transformer, 40 watts, 1939	2	10			
1030	Electric 0-4-0 (O), 1932	60	100			
1035	Steam 0-4-0 (O), 1932	65	110			
1045	Watchman, 1938-42	10	30			
1050	Pass. Car Trailer (2-7/8"), 05	3500	5750			
1100	Handcar, Mickey Mouse (O) 1935-37*	400	575			
1100	Trailer, matches 101 (Std.)	NRS	NRS			

		Good	Exc	Color	Cond	$
1103	Handcar, Peter Rabbit (O), 1935-37*	400	975	___	___	___
1105	Handcar, Santa Claus (O), 35-36*	575	1050	___	___	___
1107	Transformer in Tin Station, 1933	15	45	___	___	___
1107	Handcar, Donald Duck (O), 1936-37*	450	900	___	___	___
1121	Switches, pair (O27), 1937-42	15	35	___	___	___
1506L	Steam 0-4-0 (O), 1933-34	90	130	___	___	___
1506M	Steam 0-4-0 (O), 1935	225	450	___	___	___
1508	Steam 0-4-0, Commodore Vanderbilt w/Mickey in 1509 Stoker Tender	275	450	___	___	___
1511	Steam 0-4-0 (O), 1936-37	100	170	___	___	___
1512	Gondola (O), 1931-33, 1936-37	10	18	___	___	___
1514	Boxcar (O), 1931-37	10	18	___	___	___
1515	Tank Car (O), 1933-37	10	18	___	___	___
1517	Caboose (O), 1931-37	10	18	___	___	___
1518	Mickey Mouse Diner (O), 1935	35	85	___	___	___
1519	Mickey Mouse Band (O), 1935	35	85	___	___	___
1520	Mickey Mouse Animal (O), 1935	35	85	___	___	___
1536	Circus: 1508, 1509, 1518, 1519, 1520	550	950	___	___	___
1550	Switches, pair, Windup, 1933-37	2	6	___	___	___
1555	90° Crossover, Windup, 1933-37	1	3	___	___	___
1560	Station, 1933-37	12	25	___	___	___
1569	Accessory Set, eight pieces, 33-37	20	50	___	___	___
1588	Steam 0-4-0 (O), 1936-37	100	170	___	___	___
1630	Pullman (O), 1938-42	15	30	___	___	___
1631	Observation (O), 1938-42	15	30	___	___	___
1651E	Electric 0-4-0 (O), 1933	100	170	___	___	___
1661E	Steam 2-4-0 (O), 1933	65	130	___	___	___
1662	Steam 0-4-0 (O27), 1940-42	130	225	___	___	___
1663	Steam 0-4-0 (O27), 1940-42	160	290	___	___	___
1664/1664E	Steam 2-4-2 (O27), 38-42	45	80	___	___	___
1666/1666E	Steam 2-6-2 (O27), 38-42	55	90	___	___	___
1668/1668E	Steam 2-6-2 (O27), 37-41	60	120	___	___	___
1673	Coach (O), 1936-37	20	40	___	___	___
1674	Pullman (O), 1936-37	20	40	___	___	___
1675	Observation (O), 1936-37	20	40	___	___	___
1677	Gondola (O), 1933-35	10	35	___	___	___
1679	Boxcar (O), 1933-42	5	20	___	___	___
1680	Tank Car (O), 1933-42	5	20	___	___	___
1681E	Steam 2-4-0 (O), 1934-35	30	80	___	___	___
1681	Steam 2-4-0 (O), 1934-35	30	80	___	___	___
1682	Caboose (O), 1933-42	5	20	___	___	___
1684	Steam 2-4-2 (O), 1942	30	60	___	___	___
1685	Coach (O), uncatalogued	100	225	___	___	___
1686	Baggage (O), uncatalogued	100	225	___	___	___
1687	Observation (O), uncatalogued	100	225	___	___	___

		Good	Exc	Color	Cond	$
1688/1688E	Steam 2-4-2 (O27), 1936	30	60			
1689E	Steam 2-4-2 (O27), 1936-37	50	80			
1690	Pullman (O), 1933-34	15	30			
1691	Observation (O)	15	30			
1692	Pullman (O), 1939, uncatalogued	25	50			
1693	Observation (O), uncatalogued	25	50			
1700E	Diesel, power unit only (O)	20	45			
1700E	Set: 1700, (2) 1701s,					
	1702 (O), 1935-37	55	150			
1701	Coach (O), 1935-37	10	30			
1702	Observation (O), 1935	10	30			
1703	Obs. w/hooked coupler, uncat.	35	85			
1717	Gondola (O), 1933-40, uncat.	10	25			
1717X	Gondola (O), 1940, uncat.	10	35			
1719	Boxcar (O), 1933-40, uncat.	15	30			
1719X	Boxcar (O), 1941-42, uncat.	15	30			
1722	Caboose (O), 1933-42, uncat.	15	30			
1722X	Caboose (O), 1939-40, uncat.	8	25			
1766	Pullman (Standard), 1934-40*	300	575			
1767	Baggage (Standard), 1934-40*	300	575			
1768	Observation (Std.), 1934-40*	300	575			
1811	Pullman (O), 1933-37	10	35			
1812	Observation (O), 1933-37	25	60			
1813	Baggage (O)	50	120			
1816/1816W	Diesel (O), 1935-37	65	225			
1817	Coach (O), 1935-37	20	50			
1818	Observation (O), 1935-37	20	50			
1835E	Steam 2-4-2 (Std.), 1934-39	400	700			
1910	Elec. 0-6-0, Early (Std.), 10-11	750	1850			
1910	Electric 0-6-0, Late (Std.), 1912	450	1150			
1910	Pullman (Standard), 1909-10	800	1700			
1911	Elec. 0-4-0, Early (Std.)1910-12	1000	2300			
1911	Electric 0-4-0, Late (Std.), 1913	700	1375			
1911	Electric 0-4-4-0 Special (Std.),					
	1911-12	1000	2300			
1912	Electric 0-4-4-0 (Std.), 10-12	1500	3100			
1912	Electric 0-4-4-0 Special (Standard),					
	1911*	2000	5750			
2200	Trailer, matches 202 (Standard)	1100	2875			
2600	Pullman (O), 1938-42	45	120			
2601	Observation (O), 1938-42	45	120			
2602	Baggage (O), 1938-42	65	140			
2613	Pullman (O), 1938-42*	90	225			
2614	Observation (O), 1938-42*	90	225			
2615	Baggage (O), 1938-42*	115	250			
2620	Floodlight (O), 1938-42	18	50			
2623	Pullman (O), 1941-42	90	225			
2624	Pullman (O), 1941-42	700	1700			

		Good	Exc	Color	Cond	$
2630	Pullman (O), 1938-42	15	50			
2631	Observation (O), 1938-42	15	50			
2640	Pullman, illuminated (O), 38-42	20	40			
2641	Observation, illum. (O), 38-42	20	40			
2642	Pullman (O), 1941-42	15	35			
2643	Observation (O), 1941-42	15	35			
2651	Flatcar (O), 1938-42	15	40			
2652	Gondola (O), 1938-41	10	35			
2653	Hopper Car (O), 1938-42	20	50			
2654	Tank Car (O), 1938-42	10	40			
2655	Boxcar (O), 1938-39	20	60			
2656	Stock Car (O), 1938-39	30	70			
2657	Caboose (O), 1940-41	10	25			
2657X	Caboose (O), 1940-41	10	25			
2659	Dump Car (O)	25	45			
2660	Crane (O), 1938-42	21	50			
2672	Caboose (O), 1942	10	25			
2677	Gondola (O)	9	20			
2679	Boxcar (O)	9	25			
2680	Tank Car (O), 1938-42	9	25			
2682	Caboose (O), 1938-42	10	25			
2682X	Caboose (O), 1938-42	10	25			
2717	Gondola (O), uncatalogued	15	35			
2719	Boxcar (O), uncatalogued	15	35			
2722	Caboose (O), uncatalogued	14	35			
2755	Tank Car (O), 1941-42	25	70			
2757	Caboose (O), 1941-42	20	35			
2757X	Caboose (O), 1941-42	20	35			
2758	Automobile Boxcar (O), 1941-42	25	40			
2810	Crane (O), 1938-42	90	200			
2811	Flatcar (O), 1938-42	60	140			
2812	Gondola (O), 1938-42	30	75			
2813	Stock Car (O), 1938-42	100	200			
2814	Boxcar (O), 1938-42	80	160			
2814R	Refrigerator Car (O), 1938-42	200	350			
2815	Tank Car (O), 1938-42	45	110			
2816	Hopper Car (O), 1935-42	75	175			
2817	Caboose (O), 1936-42	35	85			
2820	Floodlight Car (O), 1938-42	75	175			
2954	Boxcar (O), 1940-42*	200	515			
2955	Sunoco Tank Car (O), 1940-42*	200	575			
2956	Hopper Car (O), 1940-42*	200	485			
2957	Caboose (O), 1940-42*	200	485			
3300	Trailer	1400	3450			
3651	Oper. Lumber Car (O), 1939-42	10	25			
3652	Operating Gondola (O), 1939-42	17	45			
3659	Oper. Dump Car (O), 1939-42	11	25			
3811	Oper. Lumber Car (O), 1939-42	25	60			

Prewar		Good	Exc	Color	Cond	$
3814	Oper. Merch. Car (O), 1929-42	90	225			
3859	Oper. Dump Car (O), 1938-42	20	60			
5344	(See 700E)					
8976	(See 227, 228, 229, 230, 706, 708)					
A	Miniature Motor, 1904	50	110			
A	Transformer, 40 or 60 watts, 1927-37	5	20			
B	New Departure Motor, 1906-16	50	110			
B	Transformer, 50 or 75 watts, 1916-38	5	20			
C	New Departure Motor, 1906-16	50	110			
D	New Departure Motor, 1906-14	50	110			
E	New Departure Motor, 1906-14	50	110			
F	New Departure Motor, 1906-14	50	110			
G	Battery Fan Motor, 1906-14	50	110			
K	Power Motor, 1904-06	50	110			
K	Transformer, 150 or 200 watts	10	25			
L	Power Motor, 1905	50	110			
L	Transformer, 50 or 75 watts	5	20			
M	Battery Motor, 1915-20	30	85			
N	Transformer, 50 watts	5	20			
Q	Transformer, 50 watts	5	20			
Q	Transformer, 75 watts	10	20			
R	Battery Motor, 1915-20	30	85			
R	Transformer, 100 watts, 1938-42	15	35			
S	Transformer, 50 watts	5	20			
S	Transformer, 80 watts	10	25			
T	Transformer, 75, 100, or 150 watts	5	20			
U	Transformer, Alladin	5	15			
V	Transformer, 150 watts, 1939-42	50	100			
W	Transformer, 75 watts	5	20			
Y	Battery Motor, 1915-20	40	90			
Z	Transformer, 250 watts, 1939-42	75	125			

Other transformers and rheostats made by Lionel:

		Good	Exc	Color	Cond	$
106	Rheostat, 1911-14	3	10			
1029	25 watts, 1936	5	15			
1030	40 watts, 1935-38	5	20			
1031	Rheosat, circa 1938	2	4			
1036	Rheostat, circa 1941	2	4			
1037	40 watts, 1940-42	5	20			
1038	Rheostat, circa 1940	2	4			
1039	35 watts, 1937-40	5	15			
1040	60 watts, 1937-39	10	25			
1041	60 watts, 1939-42	10	25			

TRACK, LOCKONS, AND CONTACTORS

	Good	Exc	Color	Cond	$
O Straight	.20	.75			
O Curve	.15	.75			

Prewar	Good	Exc	Color	Cond	$
O72 Straight	1	2.50	____	____	____
O72 Curve	1	2.50	____	____	____
O27 Straight	.10	.50	____	____	____
O27 Curve	.10	.50	____	____	____
Standard Straight	.50	2	____	____	____
Standard Curve	.50	2	____	____	____
O Gauge Lockon	.10	.50	____	____	____
Standard Gauge Lockon	.25	1	____	____	____
UTC Lockon	.25	.75	____	____	____
145C Contactor	.50	2	____	____	____
153C Contactor	.50	3	____	____	____

		Good	Exc	Color	Cond	$
011-11	Fiber Pins (O), 1946-50	.10	.15			
011-43	Insulating Pins, dz. (O), 1961	1	2			
020	90° Crossover (O), 1945-61	2	5			
020X	45° Crossover (O), 1946-59	1.50	4			
022	R.C. Switches, pair (O), 1945-49	25	55			
022-500	Adapter Set (O), 1957-61	1	2			
022A	R.C. Switches, pair (O)	—	100			
025	Bumper (O), 1946-47	5	10			
026	Bumper, 1948-50	5	10			
027C-1	Track Clips, dz. (O27), 47, 49	1	2			
30	Water Tower, 1947-50	30	85			
31	Curved Track (Super O), 1957-66	.50	.65			
31-7	Power Blade Con. (Sup. O), 57-61	—	.25			
31-15	Ground Rail Pin (Sup. O), 57-66	—	.75			
31-45	Power Blade Connection (Super O), 1961-66	—	.75			
32	Straight Track (Super O), 1957	.35	.75			
32-10	Insulating Pin (Sup. O), 1957-60	—	.50			
32-20	Power Blade Ins. (Sup. O), 57-60	—	.10			
32-25	Insulating Pin (Super O)	—	.10			
32-30	Ground Pin (Super O)	—	.10			
32-31	Power Pin (Super O)	—	.10			
32-32	Insulating Pin (Super O)	—	.10			
32-33	Ground Pin (Super O)	—	.10			
32-34	Power Pin (Super O)	—	.10			
32-45	Power Blade Insulator, dozen (Super O), 1961-66	1	2			
32-55	Ins. Pins, dz. (Super O), 1961-66	1	2			
33	Half Curved Track (Sup. O), 57-66	.50	.85			
34	Half Straight Track (Sup. O), 57-66	.50	.85			
35	Boulevard Lamp, 1945-49	10	30			
36	Rem. Control Set (Sup. O), 1957-66	2	6			
37	Uncoupling Trk. Set (Sup. O), 57-66	3	10			
38	Water Tower, 1946-47	50	250			
38	Acc. Adapter Track (Sup. O), 57-61	3	10			
39	Operating Set (Super O), 1957	2	5			
39-25	Operating Set (Sup. O), 1961-66	2	5			
40	Hookup Wire, 1950-51, 1953-63	1	3			
40-25	Conductor Wire, 1956-59	2	4			
40-50	Cable Reel, 1960-61	1	3			
41	Contactor (Super O)	.40	.80			
41	U. S. Army Switcher, 1955-57	45	95			
42	Picatinny Arsenal Switcher, 1957	80	200			
042/42	Manual Switches, pr. (O), 46-59	10	35			

		Good	Exc	Color	Cond	$
43	Power Track (Super O), 1959-66	2	4			
44-80	Missiles, 1959-60	3	7			
44	U. S. Army Mobile Launcher, 59-62	60	150			
45	U. S. Marines Mobile Launcher, 1960-62	75	250			
45	Automatic Gateman, 1946-49	15	40			
45N	Automatic Gateman, 1945	15	40			
48	Ins. Straight Track (Sup. O), 57-66	2	6			
49	Ins. Curved Track (Sup. O), 57-66	2	6			
50	Lionel Gang Car, 1954-64	20	50			
51	Navy Yard Switcher, 1956-57	65	150			
52	Fire Car, 1958-61	100	225			
53	Rio Grande Snowplow, 1957-60					
(A)	Backwards "a" in Rio Grande	100	300			
(B)	Correctly printed "a"	200	500			
54	Ballast Tamper, 1958-61, 66, 68-69	100	200			
54-6446	N & W Quad Hopper, 1954	15	45			
54-6446	N & W Cement, gray	15	45			
55-150	Ties, 1957-60	1.50	3			
55	Tie-jector, 1957-61	100	175			
56	Lamp Post, 1946-49	10	35			
56	M & St L Mine Transport, 1958	175	500			
57	A E C Switcher, 1959-60	250	675			
58	Lamp Post, 1946-50	10	40			
58	G N Snowplow, 1959-61	275	600			
59	Minuteman Switcher, 1962-63	225	550			
60	Lionelville Trolley, 1955-58	50	125			
(A)	Black lettered					
(B)	Blue lettered					
61	Ground Lockon (Sup. O), 1957-66	.25	.50			
62	Power Lockon (Sup. O), 1957-66	.25	.50			
64	Street Lamp, 1945-49	15	45			
65	Lionel Lines Handcar, 1962-66	100	325			
68	Executive Inspection Car, 1958-61	100	250			
69	Lionel Maintenance Car, 1960-62	150	300			
70	Yard Light, 1949-50	10	35			
71	Lamp Post, 1949-59	2	10			
75	Goose Neck Lamp, 1961-63	5	15			
76	Blvd. Street Lamp, 1955-56, 68-69	3	10			
80	Controller	NRS	NRS			
88	Controller, 1946-60	.50	1			
89	Flagpole, 1956-58	10	30			
90	Controller	.25	.75			
91	Circuit Breaker, 1957-60	5	10			
92	Circuit Breaker, 1959-66, 68-69	.50	1			
93	Water Tower, 1946-49	7	25			
96C	Controller	—	2			
97	Coal Elevator, 1946-50	50	150			

Postwar		Good	Exc	Color	Cond	$
100	Multivolt-DC/AC, Trans., 58-66	NRS	NRS			
109	Partial Trestle Set, 1961	NRS	NRS			
110	Graduated Trestle Set, 1955-69	3	15			
111	Elevated Trestle Set, 1956-69	3	8			
111-100	Two Elevated Trestle Piers, 1960-63	1	3			
112	R.C. Switches, pr. (Sup. O), 57-66	30	80			
114	Newsstand with horn, 1957-59	20	75			
115	Passenger Station, 1946-49	100	250			
118	Newsstand with whistle, 1957-58	20	75			
119	Landscaped Tunnel, 1957-58	NRS	NRS			
120	90° Crossing (Super O), 1957-66	2	8			
121	Landscaped Tunnel, 1959-66	NRS	NRS			
122	Lamp Assortment	NRS	NRS			
123	Lamp Assortment, 1955-59	NRS	NRS			
123-60	Lamp Assortment, 1960-63	NRS	NRS			
125	Whistle Shack, 1950-55	10	30			
128	Animated Newsstand, 1957-60	50	150			
130	60° Crossing (Super O), 1957-61	2	8			
131	Curved Tunnel, 1959-66	NRS	NRS			
132	Passenger Station, 1949-55	25	75			
133	Passenger Station, 1957-66	20	60			
137	Passenger Station, 1946 (See Prewar section)	Not Manufactured				
138	Water Tower, 1953-57	35	70			
140	Automatic Banjo Signal, 1954-66	5	25			
142	Man. Switches, pr. (Sup. O), 57-66	20	40			
145C	Contactor, 1950-60	.50	1.50			
145	Automatic Gateman, 1950-66	15	30			
147	Whistle Controller, 1961-66	.50	1			
148	Dwarf Trackside Signal, 1957-60	15	50			
150	Telegraph Pole Set, 1947-50	10	35			
151	Automatic Semaphore, 1947-69	10	25			
152	Automatic Crossing Gate, 1945-49	10	20			
153	Auto. Block Control, Signal, 45-59	10	20			
153C	Contactor	.50	2			
154	Auto Highway Signal, 1945-69	10	30			
155	Blinking Light Signal w/bell, 55-57	10	30			
156	Station Platform, 1946-49	15	40			
157	Station Platform, 1952-59	10	25			
160	Unloading Bin, 1952-57	.25	1			
161	Mail Pickup Set, 1961-63	20	75			
163	Single Target Block Signal, 61-69	10	20			
164	Log Loader, 1946-50	65	150			
167	Whistle Controller, 1945-46	1	3			
175	Rocket Launcher, 1958-60	50	200			
175-50	Extra Rocket, 1959-60	3	10			
182	Magnetic Crane, 1946-49	75	150			
192	Operating Control Tower, 1959-60	50	150			

		Good	Exc	Color	Cond	$
193	Industrial Water Tower, 1953-55	25	60			
195	Floodlight Tower, 1957-69	10	25			
195-75	Eight-Bulb Extension, 1958-60	5	15			
196	Smoke Pellets, 1946-47	—	20			
197	Rotating Radar Antenna, 1958-59	20	65			
199	Microwave/Relay Tower, 1958-59	20	65			
202	U P Alco A unit, 1957	25	75			
204	Santa Fe Alco AA units, 1957	50	125			
205	M P Alco AA units, 1957-58	50	125			
206	Artificial Coal, large bag, 1946-68	—	8			
207	Artificial Coal, small bag	—	5			
208	Santa Fe Alco AA units, 1958-59	50	150			
209	New Haven Alco AA units, 1958	200	600			
209	Wooden Barrels, set of four, 46-50	—	5			
210	Texas Special Alco AA units, 58	50	150			
211	Texas Spec. Alco AA units, 62-66	50	120			
212	U. S. M. C. Alco A, 1958-59	50	135			
212	Santa Fe Alco AA units, 1964-66	50	150			
212T	U. S. M. C. dum. A unit, 58-59	200	475			
213	Railroad Lift Bridge, 1950			Not Manufactured		
213	M & St L Alco AA units, 1964	50	150			
214	Plate Girder Bridge, 1953-69	5	15			
215	Santa Fe Alco units, 1965					
(A)	AB units	50	150			
(B)	Double A units	50	125			
216	Burlington Alco A unit, 1958	75	250			
216	M & St L Alco A unit	75	150			
217	B & M Alco AB units, 1959	50	150			
218	Santa Fe Alco units, 1959-63					
(A)	Double A units	60	125			
(B)	AB units	60	125			
219	M P Alco AA units, 1959	50	125			
220	Santa Fe Alco units, 1960-61					
(A)	A unit only	50	125			
(B)	AA units	75	200			
221	2-6-4, 221T/221W Tender, 46-47	40	75			
221	Rio Grande Alco A unit, 1963-64	35	75			
221	U. S. M. C. Alco A unit, 1963-64	75	225			
221	Santa Fe Alco A unit, 1963-64	100	350			
222	Rio Grande Alco A unit, 1962	35	75			
223	218C Santa Fe Alco AB units, 63	50	150			
224	Steam 2-6-2, 2466T/2466W Tender, 1945-46	50	75			
224	U. S. Navy Alco AB units, 1960	75	175			
225	C & O Alco A unit, 1960	40	100			
226	B & M Alco AB units, 1960	50	125			
227	C N Alco A unit, 1960	50	125			
228	C N Alco A unit, 1961	50	100			

		Good	Exc	Color	Cond	$
229	M & St L Alco units, 1961-62					
(A)	1961, A unit only	50	100			
(B)	1962, AB units	75	150			
230	C & O Alco A unit, 1961	50	100			
231	Alco A unit, 1961-63	50	125			
232	New Haven Alco A unit, 1962	50	90			
233	Steam 2-4-2, 233W Tender, 61-62	35	50			
235	Steam 2-4-2, 1130T/1060T Tender, 1961, uncatalogued	15	30			
236	Steam 2-4-2, 1130T/1050T Tender, 1961-62	10	25			
237	Steam 2-4-2, 1963-66					
(A)	With 1060T Tender	10	25			
(B)	With 234W Tender	35	50			
238	Steam 2-4-2, 234W Tender, 63-64	35	50			
239	Steam 2-4-2, 234W Tender, 65-66	35	50			
240	Steam 2-4-2, 1964, uncatalogued	100	200			
241	Steam 2-4-2, 1965, uncatalogued					
(A)	With 1130T Tender	25	40			
(B)	With 234W Tender	35	50			
242	Steam 2-4-2, 1962-66					
(A)	With 1060T Tender	20	30			
(B)	With 1062T Tender	15	25			
243	Steam 2-4-2, 243W Tender, 1960	35	50			
244	Steam 2-4-2, 244T/1130T Tender, 1960-61	15	25			
245	Steam 2-4-2, with 1060T Tender, 1959-60, uncatalogued	15	25			
246	Steam 2-4-2, 244T/1130T Tender, 1959-61	15	30			
247	Steam 2-4-2, 247T Tender, 1959	20	40			
248	Steam 2-4-2, 1130T Tender, 1958	15	40			
249	Steam 2-4-2, 250T Tender, 1958	15	40			
250	Steam 2-4-2, 250T Tender, 1957	15	40			
251	Steam 2-4-2, 1062T Tender, 1966, uncatalogued	50	100			
252	Crossing Gate, 1950-62	10	20			
253	Block Control Signal, 1956-59	10	30			
256	Operating Freight Station, 1950-53	10	30			
257	Freight Sta. w/diesel horn, 1956-57	20	65			
260	Bumper, 1951-69					
(A)	Die-cast	5	10			
(B)	Black plastic	20	40			
262	Highway Crossing Gate, 1962-69	10	30			
264	Operating Fork Lift Platform, includes 6264, 1957-60	50	140			
270	Metal Bridge (O)	15	30			
282	Gantry Crane, 1954-57	60	150			

	Good	Exc	ColorCond $
282R Gantry Crane, 1956-57	60	150	___ ___ ___
299 Code Transmitter Beacon Set, 1961-63	50	100	___ ___ ___
308 Railroad Sign Set, 1945-49	10	20	___ ___ ___
309 Yard Sign Set, die-cast, 1950-59	5	15	___ ___ ___
310 Billboard, 1950-68	5	15	___ ___ ___
313 Bascule Bridge, 1946-49	150	350	___ ___ ___
313-82 Fiber Pins, 1946-60	.05	.05	___ ___ ___
313-121 Fiber Pins, 1961	—	1.50	___ ___ ___
314 Scale Model Girder Bridge, 45-50	5	15	___ ___ ___
315 Trestle Bridge, 1946-48	25	50	___ ___ ___
316 Trestle Bridge, 1949	10	30	___ ___ ___
317 Trestle Bridge, 1950-56	5	15	___ ___ ___
321 Trestle Bridge, 1958-64	5	7	___ ___ ___
332 Arch-Under Bridge, 1959-66	10	30	___ ___ ___
334 Oper. Dispatching Board, 1957-60	50	125	___ ___ ___
(334) Missile Launching Car, olive drab, 1963-64	60	275	___ ___ ___
342 Culvert Loader, 1956-58	50	150	___ ___ ___
345 Culvert Unloader, 1957-59	75	225	___ ___ ___
346 Manual Culvert Unloader, 1965	50	150	___ ___ ___
347 Cannon Firing Range Set, 1964, uncatalogued	75	175	___ ___ ___
348 Manual Culvert Unloader, 1966-69	50	150	___ ___ ___
350 Engine Transfer Table, 1957-60	100	225	___ ___ ___
350-50 Transfer Table Extension, 57-60	25	100	___ ___ ___
352 Ice Depot, includes 6352, 1955-57	50	125	___ ___ ___
353 Trackside Control Signal, 1960-61	10	30	___ ___ ___
356 Operating Freight Station, 1952-57	25	75	___ ___ ___
362 Barrel Loader, 1952-57	30	60	___ ___ ___
362-78 Wooden Barrels, 1952-57	2	6	___ ___ ___
364 Conveyor Lumber Loader, 1948-57	50	100	___ ___ ___
364C On/Off Switch, 1948-64	1	2	___ ___ ___
365 Dispatching Station, 1958-59	35	75	___ ___ ___
375 Turntable, 1962-64	50	150	___ ___ ___
390C Switch, d.p.d.t., 1960-64	.50	2	___ ___ ___
394 Rotary Beacon, 1949-53	15	40	___ ___ ___
395 Floodlight Tower, 1949-56	10	30	___ ___ ___
397 Diesel Oper. Coal Loader, 1948-57	50	100	___ ___ ___
400 B & O RDC Pass. Car, 1956-58	100	200	___ ___ ___
404 B & O RDC Baggage-Mail, 1957-58	150	350	___ ___ ___
410 Billboard Blinker, 1956-58	20	45	___ ___ ___
413 Countdown Control Panel, 1962	10	20	___ ___ ___
415 Diesel Fueling Station, 1955-57	50	125	___ ___ ___
419 Heliport Control Tower, 1962	75	250	___ ___ ___
443 Missile Launch Platform, with 943 ammo dump, 1960-62	10	20	___ ___ ___

		Good	Exc	ColorCond $
445	Switch Tower, lighted, 1952-57	20	50	___ ___ ___
448	Missile Firing Range Set, with 6448, 1961-63	50	100	___ ___ ___
450	Signal Bridge, two-track, 1952-58	15	40	___ ___ ___
450L	Signal Light Head	10	20	___ ___ ___
452	Signal Bridge, single-track, 61-63	50	100	___ ___ ___
455	Operating Oil Derrick, 1950-54	50	100	___ ___ ___
456	Coal Ramp/ 3456 Hopper, 1950-55	50	100	___ ___ ___
460	Piggyback Transportation, includes 3460, 1955-57	50	100	___ ___ ___
460P	Piggyback Platform, 1955-57	20	40	___ ___ ___
461	Platform with Truck and Trailer, 66	50	100	___ ___ ___
462	Derrick Platform Set, 1961-62	50	175	___ ___ ___
464	Lumber Mill, 1956-60	30	90	___ ___ ___
465	Sound Dispatching Station, 56-57	30	60	___ ___ ___
470	Missile Launching Platform with 6470, 1959-62	50	100	___ ___ ___
480-25	Conversion Coupler, 1950-60	—	2	___ ___ ___
480-32	Conv. Magnetic Coupler, 61-69	—	2	___ ___ ___
494	Rotary Beacon, 1954-66	10	30	___ ___ ___
497	Coaling Station, 1953-58	50	125	___ ___ ___
520	Lionel Lines Box Cab Electric, 1956-57	35	90	___ ___ ___
600	M K T NW-2 Switcher, 1955			
(A)	Black frame and end rails	75	150	___ ___ ___
(B)	Gray frame and yellow end rails	125	350	___ ___ ___
601	Seaboard NW-2 Switcher, 1956	75	150	___ ___ ___
602	Seaboard NW-2 Switcher, 1957-58	90	175	___ ___ ___
610	Erie NW-2 Switcher, 1955			
(A)	Black frame	75	150	___ ___ ___
(B)	Yellow frame	125	350	___ ___ ___
611	Jersey Central NW-2, 1957-58	75	150	___ ___ ___
613	U P NW-2 Switcher, 1958	125	350	___ ___ ___
614	Alaska NW-2 Switcher, 1959-60	100	180	___ ___ ___
616	Santa Fe NW-2, 1961-62	75	175	___ ___ ___
617	Santa Fe NW-2 Switcher, 1963	100	200	___ ___ ___
621	Jersey Central NW-2, 1956-57	50	125	___ ___ ___
622	S F NW-2 Switcher, 1949-50	100	275	___ ___ ___
623	S F NW-2 Switcher, 1952-54	75	200	___ ___ ___
624	C & O NW-2 Switcher, 1952-54	125	250	___ ___ ___
625	L V GE 44-ton Switcher, 1957-58	50	130	___ ___ ___
626	B & O GE 44-ton Switcher, 1959	75	300	___ ___ ___
627	L V GE 44-ton Switcher, 56-57	75	125	___ ___ ___
628	N P GE 44-ton Switcher, 56-57	75	125	___ ___ ___
629	Burlington GE 44-ton, 1956	75	300	___ ___ ___
633	Santa Fe NW-2 Switcher, 1962	50	100	___ ___ ___
634	Santa Fe NW-2, 1963, 1965-66	50	100	___ ___ ___
635	U P NW-2 Switcher, 1965, uncat.	40	90	___ ___ ___

		Good	Exc	ColorCond $
37	Steam 2-6-4, 2046W/736W Tender, 1959-63	40	85	___ ___ ___
38-2361	Van Camps Pork & Beans Boxcar, 1962, uncatalogued	10	20	___ ___ ___
45	Union Pacific NW-2 Switcher, 69	40	90	___ ___ ___
46	Steam 4-6-4, 2046W Tdr., 1954-58	75	175	___ ___ ___
65	Steam 4-6-4, 2046W/6026W/736W Tender, 1954-59, 1966	60	135	___ ___ ___
70	Pennsylvania Turbine, 6-8-6, 1952		Not Manufactured	
71R	Steam 6-8-6, 4424W/4671 Tender, 1946-49	100	250	___ ___ ___
71	Steam 6-8-6, 1946-49			
(A)	671W Tender	75	150	___ ___ ___
(B)	2671W Tender	100	250	___ ___ ___
71RR	Steam 6-8-6, 2046W-50 Tender, 1952	75	150	___ ___ ___
71S	Smoke Conversion Kit	—	35	___ ___ ___
74	Steam 2-6-4, 1952		Not Manufactured	
75	Steam 2-6-2, 2466W/2466WX/ 6466WX Tender, 1947-49, 1952	45	90	___ ___ ___
81	Steam Turbine, 6-8-6, 2046W-50/2671W Tender, 1950-51, 1953	75	170	___ ___ ___
82	Steam 6-8-6, 2046W-50 Tender, 1954-55	150	300	___ ___ ___
85	Steam 4-6-4, 6026W Tender, 1953	75	175	___ ___ ___
86	Steam 4-6-4, circa 1953-54	NRS	NRS	___ ___ ___
703	Steam 4-6-4, Hudson, 1946		Not Manufactured	
703-10	Special Smoke Bulb, 1946	—	20	___ ___ ___
711	Rem. Cont. O72 Switches	100	200	___ ___ ___
721	Manual O72 Switches	50	100	___ ___ ___
725	Steam 2-8-4, Berkshire, 1952		Not Manufactured	
726	(A) Steam 2-8-4 Berkshire, 2426W Tender, 1946	200	375	___ ___ ___
726	(B) (C) Steam 2-8-4, 2426W Tender, 1947-49	175	325	___ ___ ___
726RR	Steam 2-8-4 Berkshire, 2046W Tender, 1952	100	225	___ ___ ___
726S	Smoke Conversion Kit	NRS	NRS	___ ___ ___
736	2-8-4, 2671WX/2046W/736W Tender, 1950-66	175	275	___ ___ ___
746	N & W Steam 4-8-4, 1957-60			
(A)	Long stripe Tender, 1957	400	1000	___ ___ ___
(B)	Short stripe Tender, 1958-60	500	1200	___ ___ ___
760	Curved Trk., 16 sec. (O72), 54-57	15	35	___ ___ ___
773	Steam 4-6-4, 2426W Tdr., 1950	475	1100	___ ___ ___
773	Steam 4-6-4, 1964-66			
(A)	With 773W Tender	400	775	___ ___ ___
(B)	With 736W Tender	400	800	___ ___ ___

		Good	Exc	Color	Cond	$
902	Elevated Trestle Set, 1960	NRS	NRS	___	___	___
909	Smoke Fluid, 1957-68	—	5	___	___	___
919	Artificial Grass, 1946-64	—	5	___	___	___
920	Scenic Display Set, 1957-58	25	75	___	___	___
920-2	Tunnel Portals, pair, 1958-59	10	20	___	___	___
920-3	Green grass, 1957	—	8	___	___	___
920-4	Yellow grass, 1957	—	8	___	___	___
920-5	Artificial Rock, 1958	.50	2	___	___	___
920-8	Lichen, 1958	.50	2	___	___	___
925	Lionel Lubricant, lg. tube, 1946-69	.50	3	___	___	___
926	Lionel Lubricant, sm. tube, 1955	.25	2	___	___	___
926-5	Instruction Booklet, 1946-48	.25	1	___	___	___
927	Lubricating Kit, 1950-59	10	15	___	___	___
928	Maint. & Lubricating Kit, 1960-63	15	25	___	___	___
943	Ammo Dump, 1959-61	10	20	___	___	___
950	U. S. Railroad Map, 1958-66	10	20	___	___	___
951	Farm Set, 1958	10	25	___	___	___
952	Miniature Figure Set, 1958	10	25	___	___	___
953	Miniature Figure Set, 1960-62	10	25	___	___	___
954	Swimming Pool/Playground Set, 59	10	25	___	___	___
955	Farm Building and Animal Set, 58	10	25	___	___	___
956	Stockyard Set, 1959	10	25	___	___	___
957	Farm Building and Animal Set, 58	10	25	___	___	___
958	Vehicle Set, 1958	10	25	___	___	___
959	Barn Set, 1958	10	25	___	___	___
960	Barnyard Set, 1959-61	10	25	___	___	___
961	School Set, 1959	10	25	___	___	___
962	Turnpike Set, 1958	10	25	___	___	___
963	Frontier Set, 1959-60	10	25	___	___	___
963-100	Box for Halloween General Set	50	125	___	___	___
964	Factory Set, 1959	10	25	___	___	___
965	Farm Set, 1959	10	25	___	___	___
966	Fire House Set, 1958	10	25	___	___	___
967	Post Office Set, 1958	10	25	___	___	___
968	TV Transmitter Set, 1958	10	25	___	___	___
969	Construction Set, 1960	10	25	___	___	___
970	Ticket Booth, 1958-60	25	75	___	___	___
971	Lichen Package, 1960-64	2	4	___	___	___
972	Landscape Tree Assortment, 61-64	2	4	___	___	___
973	Complete Landscaping Set, 60-64	3	6	___	___	___
974	Scenery Set, 1962-63	4	8	___	___	___
980	Ranch Set, 1960	10	25	___	___	___
981	Freight Yard Set, 1960	10	25	___	___	___
982	Suburban Split Level Set, 1960	10	25	___	___	___
983	Farm Set, 1960-61	10	25	___	___	___
984	Railroad Set, 1961-62	10	25	___	___	___
985	Freight Area Set, 1961	10	25	___	___	___
986	Farm Set, 1962	10	25	___	___	___

		Good	Exc	ColorCond $
987	Town Set, 1962	10	25	___ ___ ___
988	Railroad Structure Set, 1962	10	25	___ ___ ___
1001	Steam 2-4-2, 1001T Tender, 1948	10	25	___ ___ ___
1002	Lionel Gondola, 1948-52			
(A)	Black unpainted plastic, white lettering	3	7	___ ___ ___
(B)	Blue unpainted plastic, white lettering	4	10	___ ___ ___
(C)	Silver w/black lettering	100	300	___ ___ ___
(D)	Yellow w/black lettering	100	300	___ ___ ___
(E)	Red w/white lettering	100	300	___ ___ ___
(F)	Light blue w/black lettering	NRS	NRS	___ ___ ___
X1004	P R R Baby Ruth Boxcar, 48-52	2	4	___ ___ ___
1005	Sunoco 1-D Tank Car, 1948-50	2	5	___ ___ ___
1007	L L SP Type Caboose, 1948-52	2	5	___ ___ ___
1008	Camtrol Uncoupling Unit (O27), 1957-62	.50	1	___ ___ ___
1008-50	Uncoupling Track (O27), 48	.25	1	___ ___ ___
1010	Transformer, 35 watts, 1961-66	—	5	___ ___ ___
1011	Transformer, 25 watts, 1948-49	—	5	___ ___ ___
1012	Transformer, 35 watts, 1950-54	—	5	___ ___ ___
1013	Curved Track (O27), 1945-69	.10	.20	___ ___ ___
1013-17	Steel Pins (O27), 1946-60	—	.05	___ ___ ___
1013-42	Steel Pins (O27), 1961-68	—	.60	___ ___ ___
1014	Transformer, 40 watts, 1955	3	10	___ ___ ___
1015	Transformer, 45 watts, 1956-60	—	5	___ ___ ___
1016	Transformer, 35 watts, 1959-60	—	5	___ ___ ___
1018-1/2	Straight Track (O27), 55-69	.10	.30	___ ___ ___
1018	Straight Track (O27), 1945-69	.10	.30	___ ___ ___
1019	R.C. Track Set (O27), 1946-48	1.50	5	___ ___ ___
1020	90° Crossing (O27), 1955-69	1.50	3	___ ___ ___
1021	90° Crossing (O27), 1945-54	1.50	3	___ ___ ___
1022	Man. Switches, pr. (O27), 53-69	5	15	___ ___ ___
1023	45° Crossing (O27), 1956-69	1.50	3	___ ___ ___
1024	Man. Switches, pr. (O27), 46-52	5	15	___ ___ ___
1025	Transformer, 45 watts, 1961-69	—	5	___ ___ ___
1025	Illuminated Bumper (O27), 46-47	5	15	___ ___ ___
1026	Transformer, 25 watts, 1961-64	—	5	___ ___ ___
1032	Transformer, 75 watts, 1948	—	15	___ ___ ___
1033	Transformer, 90 watts, 1948-56	—	35	___ ___ ___
1034	Transformer, 75 watts, 1948-54	—	30	___ ___ ___
1035	Transformer, 60 watts, 1947	5	10	___ ___ ___
1037	Transformer, 40 watts, 1946-47	—	5	___ ___ ___
1041	Transformer, 60 watts, 1945-46	—	15	___ ___ ___
1042	Transformer, 75 watts, 1947-48	—	15	___ ___ ___
1043	Transformer			
(A)	50 watts, black, 1953-57	—	15	___ ___ ___
(B)	60 watts, ivory, 1957-58	—	75	___ ___ ___

		Good	Exc	ColorCond $
1044	Transformer, 90 watts, 1957-69	—	30	
1045	Operating Watchman, 1946-50	10	25	
1047	Operating Switchman, 1959-61	25	100	
1050	Steam 0-4-0, 1050 Tender (O27), 1959, uncatalogued	10	35	
1053	Transformer, 60 watts, 1956-60	—	20	
1055	Texas Spec. Alco A unit, 1959-60	25	75	
1060	Steam 2-4-2, 1050T/1060T Tender, 1960-62	12	25	
1061	Steam 0-4-0, 1061T Tender, 1964; 2-4-2, 1969	10	25	
1062	Steam 2-4-2, 1062T Tdr., 63-64	10	25	
1063	Transformer, 75 watts, 1960-64	—	20	
1065	Union Pacific Alco A unit, 1961	25	75	
1066	Union Pacific Alco A unit, 1964	25	75	
1073	Transformer, 60 watts, 1961-66	—	15	
1101	Steam 2-4-2, 1948	15	30	
1101	Transformer, 25 watts, 1948	—	5	
1110	Steam 2-4-2, 1949, 1951-52	10	25	
1120	Steam 2-4-2, 1950	15	25	
1121	R.C. Switches, pr. (O27), 1946-51	10	30	
1122	R.C. Switches, pr. (O27), 1952-53	10	30	
1122-34	R.C. Switches, pair, 1952-53	10	35	
1122-500	Gauge Adapter (O27), 57-66	.25	1	
1122E	R.C. Switches, pr. (O27), 53-69	10	35	
1130	Steam 2-4-2, 6066T/1130T Tender, 1953-54	15	25	
1615	Steam 0-4-0, 1615T Tdr., 55-57	55	140	
1625	Steam 0-4-0, 1625T Tender, 1958	65	200	
1640-100	Presidential Kit, 1960	25	75	
1654	Steam 2-4-2, 1654T/1654W Tender, 1946-47	15	30	
1655	Steam 2-4-2, 6654W Tdr., 48-49	15	35	
1656	Steam 0-4-0, 6403B Tdr., 48-49	125	225	
1665	Steam 0-4-0, 2403B Tender, 46	125	275	
1666	Steam 2-6-2, 2466W/2466WX/6654W Tender, 1946-47	20	60	
1862	General 4-4-0, 1862T Tdr., 59-62	75	175	
1865	Western & Atlantic Coach, 59-62	13	35	
1866	W & A Baggage, 1959-62	15	35	
1872	General 4-4-0, 1872T Tender, 1959-62	100	250	
1875	W & A Coach, 1959-62	75	175	
1875W	W & A Coach w/whistle, 59-62	50	100	
1876	W & A Baggage, 1959-62	25	60	
(1877)	No number, flatcar, 1960-65	3	5	
1877	Flatcar w/fence & horses, 1959-62	20	50	

		Good	Exc	ColorCond $
1882	General 4-4-0, 1882T Tender, 1960, uncatalogued	150	300	___ ___ ___
1885	Western & Atlantic Coach, 1960, uncatalogued	75	250	___ ___ ___
1887	Flatcar with fences and horses, 1960, uncatalogued	50	150	___ ___ ___
2003	Track "Make-up" Kit for "O27 Track", 1963	NRS	NRS	___ ___ ___
2016	Steam 2-6-4, 6026W Tdr., 55-56	30	80	___ ___ ___
2018	Steam 2-6-4, 1956-59, 1961			
(A)	6026T Tender	40	100	___ ___ ___
(B)	6026W Tender	80	150	___ ___ ___
(C)	1130T Tender	40	100	___ ___ ___
2020	Steam 6-8-6, 2020W/6020W Tender, 1946-49	75	140	___ ___ ___
2023	U P Alco AA, 1950-51			
(A)	Yellow body	100	250	___ ___ ___
(B)	Silver body	100	250	___ ___ ___
2024	Chesapeake & Ohio Alco A, 69	35	75	___ ___ ___
2025	Steam 2-6-2, 2-6-4, 2466W/6466W Tender, 1947-49, 1952	50	85	___ ___ ___
2026	Steam 2-6-2, 1948-49, 1951-53			
(A)	6466W or 6466WX	40	70	___ ___ ___
(B)	6466T or 6066T	40	70	___ ___ ___
2028	Pennsylvania GP-7, 1955			
(A)	Gold lettering	125	400	___ ___ ___
(B)	Yellow lettering	125	350	___ ___ ___
(C)	Tan frame	200	500	___ ___ ___
2029	Steam 2-6-4, 234W Tdr., 64-69	60	100	___ ___ ___
2031	Rock Island Alco AA, 1952-54	125	400	___ ___ ___
2032	Erie Alco AA units, 1952-54	100	225	___ ___ ___
2033	U P Alco AA, 1952-54	100	250	___ ___ ___
2034	Steam 2-4-2, 6066T Tdr., 1952	20	35	___ ___ ___
2035	Steam 2-6-4, 6466W Tdr., 50-51	50	75	___ ___ ___
2036	Steam 2-6-4, 6466W Tdr., 1950	40	70	___ ___ ___
2037	Steam 2-6-4, black engine, 1954-55, 1957-63	50	90	___ ___ ___
2037-500	Steam 2-6-4, pink engine, with 1130T-500 Tender, 1957-58	400	750	___ ___ ___
2041	Rock Island Alco AA, 1969	50	110	___ ___ ___
2046	Steam 4-6-4, 2046W Tender, 1950-51, 1953	100	175	___ ___ ___
2055	Steam 4-6-4, 2046W/6026W Tender, 1953-55	65	140	___ ___ ___
2056	Steam 4-6-4, 2046W Tdr., 1952	90	190	___ ___ ___
2065	Steam 4-6-4, 2046W/6026W Tender, 1954-56	80	140	___ ___ ___
2240	Wabash F-3 AB units, 1956	300	700	___ ___ ___

		Good	Exc	ColorCond $
2242	New Haven F-3 AB units, 58-59	400	850	___ ___ ___
2243	Santa Fe F-3 AB units, 1955-57	225	400	___ ___ ___
2243C	Santa Fe F-3 B unit, 1955-57	75	175	___ ___ ___
2245	Texas Special F-3 AB, 1954-55			
(A)	B unit with portholes, two-piece horn, 1954	225	500	___ ___ ___
(B)	B unit w/o portholes, one-piece horn, 1955	375	700	___ ___ ___
2257	Lionel SP Type caboose, 1947			
(A)	Red, no stack	3	6	___ ___ ___
(B)	Tuscan, with stack	25	75	___ ___ ___
2321	Lackawanna Trainmaster, 1954-56			
(A)	Gray roof	200	475	___ ___ ___
(B)	Maroon roof	300	700	___ ___ ___
2322	Virginian Trainmaster, 1965-66			
(A)	Unpainted blue stripe	200	575	___ ___ ___
(B)	Painted blue stripe	350	700	___ ___ ___
2328	Burlington GP-7, 1955-56	150	375	___ ___ ___
2329	Virginian Rectifier, 1958-59	250	650	___ ___ ___
2330	Pennsylvania GG-1, green, 1950	350	1500	___ ___ ___
2331	Virginian Trainmaster, 1955-58			
(A)	1955, black stripe/gold lett.	550	1250	___ ___ ___
(B)	1956-58, blue stripe/yellow lett.	350	750	___ ___ ___
(C)	Blue and yellow, gray mold	450	1000	___ ___ ___
2332	Pennsylvania GG-1, 1947-49	500	1800	___ ___ ___
2333	Santa Fe F-3 AA units, 1948-49	225	500	___ ___ ___
(A)	Rubber-stamped lettering	225	500	___ ___ ___
(B)	Heat-stamped lettering	325	900	___ ___ ___
2333	N Y C F-3 AA units, 1948-49			
(A)	Rubber-stamped lettering	500	1000	___ ___ ___
(B)	Heat-stamped lettering	225	500	___ ___ ___
2337	Wabash GP-7, 1958	100	300	___ ___ ___
2338	Milwaukee Road GP-7, 1955-56			
(A)	Orange band all around shell	750	1750	___ ___ ___
(B)	Incomplete orange band	100	225	___ ___ ___
2339	Wabash GP-7, 1957	100	250	___ ___ ___
2340	Pennsylvania GG-1, 1955			
(A)	Tuscan	350	1600	___ ___ ___
(B)	Dark green	350	1500	___ ___ ___
2341	Jersey Central Trainmaster, 1956			
(A)	High gloss orange	1000	2250	___ ___ ___
(B)	Dull orange	800	1950	___ ___ ___
2343	Santa Fe F-3 AA units, 1950-52	200	650	___ ___ ___
2343C	Santa Fe F-3 B unit, 1950-55	65	195	___ ___ ___
2344	N Y C F-3 AA units, 1950-52	250	575	___ ___ ___
2344C	N Y C F-3 B unit, 1950-55	95	235	___ ___ ___
2345	Western Pacific F-3 AA, 1952	800	1900	___ ___ ___
2346	B & M GP-9, 1965-66	100	250	___ ___ ___

		Good	Exc	Color	Cond	$
347	C & O GP-7, 1965, uncat.	1250	2750	___	___	___
348	M & St L GP-9, 1958-59	150	425	___	___	___
349	Northern Pacific GP-9, 1959-60	200	375	___	___	___
350	New Haven EP-5, 1956-58					
(A)	White "N", painted nose	350	750	___	___	___
(B)	White "N", decal nose	125	450	___	___	___
(C)	Orange "N", painted nose	950	1500	___	___	___
(D)	Orange "N", decal nose	500	1000	___	___	___
(E)	White "N", orange paint through doors	350	700	___	___	___
351	Milwaukee EP-5, 1957-58	200	500	___	___	___
352	Pennsylvania EP-5, 1958-59					
(A)	Tuscan body	225	525	___	___	___
(B)	Chocolate brown body	225	525	___	___	___
353	Santa Fe F-3 AA units, 1953-55	225	600	___	___	___
354	N Y C F-3 AA units, 1953-55	225	600	___	___	___
355	Western Pacific F-3 AA, 1953	750	1800	___	___	___
356	Southern F-3 AA units, 1954-56	450	1250	___	___	___
356C	Southern F-3 B unit, 1954-56	125	325	___	___	___
357	Lionel SP Type Caboose, 1947-48					
(A)	Red w/red stack	25	75	___	___	___
(B)	Tuscan w/tuscan stack	10	20	___	___	___
358	Great Northern EP-5, 1959-60	300	1000	___	___	___
359	Boston & Maine GP-9, 1961-62	100	250	___	___	___
360	Penn GG-1, 1956-58, 1961-63					
(A)	Tuscan, five gold stripes	350	1600	___	___	___
(B)	Dark green, five gold stripes	350	1250	___	___	___
(C)	Tuscan, single gold stripe, heat-stamped lettering	350	1500	___	___	___
(D)	Tuscan, single gold stripe, decal lettering	350	850	___	___	___
2363	Illinois Central F-3 AB, 1955-56	300	1200	___	___	___
2365	C & O GP-7, 1962-63	125	350	___	___	___
2367	Wabash F-3 AB units, 1955	325	1000	___	___	___
2368	B & O F-3 AB units, 1956	700	2200	___	___	___
2373	C P F-3 AA units, 1957	700	1800	___	___	___
2378	M R F-3 AB units, 1956					
(A)	With roof line stripes	1000	2400	___	___	___
(B)	Without roof line stripes	700	2200	___	___	___
2379	Rio Grande F-3 AB units, 57-58	400	1000	___	___	___
2383	Santa Fe F-3 AA units, 1958-66	300	550	___	___	___
2400	Maplewood Pull., green, 1948-49	50	125	___	___	___
2401	Hillside Obs., green, 1948-49	50	125	___	___	___
2402	Chatham Pullman, green, 1948-49	50	125	___	___	___
2404	Santa Fe Vista Dome, 1964-65	20	50	___	___	___
2405	Santa Fe Pullman, 1964-65	20	50	___	___	___
2406	Santa Fe Observation, 1964-65	20	50	___	___	___
2408	Santa Fe Vista Dome, 1966	20	50	___	___	___

		Good	Exc	Color	Cond	$
2409	Santa Fe Pullman, 1966	20	50			
2410	Santa Fe Observation, 1966	20	50			
2411	Flatcar w/pipes, die-cast, 1946	20	100			
2411	Flatcar w/logs, die-cast, 1947-48	10	25			
2412	Santa Fe Vista Dome, 1959-63	15	40			
2414	Santa Fe Pullman, 1959-63	20	45			
2416	Santa Fe Observation, 1959-63	15	40			
2419	D L & W Work Caboose, 46-47	15	30			
2420	D L & W Work Caboose, with light, 1946-48	25	80			
2421	Maplewood Pullman, 1950-53					
(A)	Gray roof	35	100			
(B)	Aluminum roof	30	75			
2422	Chatham Pullman, 1950-53					
(A)	Gray roof	35	100			
(B)	Aluminum roof	30	75			
2423	Hillside Observation, 1950-53					
(A)	Gray roof	35	100			
(B)	Aluminum roof	35	75			
2429	Livingston Pullman, 1952-53	50	125			
2430	Blue Pullman, 1946-47	12	25			
2431	Blue Observation, 1946-47	20	40			
2432	Clifton Vista Dome, 1954-58	15	35			
2434	Newark Pullman, 1954-58	15	35			
2435	Elizabeth Pullman, 1954-58	30	65			
2436	Summit Observation, 1954-56	25	60			
2436	Mooseheart Observation, 1957-58	30	65			
2440	Green Pullman, 1946-47	20	40			
2441	Green Observation, 1946-47	20	40			
2442	Clifton Vista Dome, 1956	45	110			
2442	Brown Pullman 1946-48	20	55			
2443	Brown Observation, 1946-48	20	55			
2444	Newark Pullman, 1956	45	110			
2445	Elizabeth Pullman, 1956	60	150			
2446	Summit Observation, 1956	45	110			
2452	Pennsylvania Gondola, 1945-47	5	15			
2452X	Pennsylvania Gondola, 1946-47	4	10			
X2454	Pennsylvania Boxcar, 1946	20	80			
X2454	Baby Ruth Boxcar, "P R R" logo, 1946-47	5	15			
2456	Lehigh Valley, 1948	5	15			
2457	Penn Cab., metal, N5, 1945-47	10	25			
X2458	Pennsylvania Boxcar, 1946-47	15	35			
2460	Bucyrus Erie Crane, 12-wheel, 1946-50					
(A)	Gray Cab	60	175			
(B)	Black Cab	35	75			
2461	Transformer Car, die-cast, 1947-48					
(A)	Red transformer	40	100			

		Good	Exc	ColorCond $
(B)	Black transformer	30	80	___ ___ ___
2465	Sunoco 2-D Tank Car, 1946-48	5	15	___ ___ ___
2472	Penn. Caboose, metal, N5, 46-47	8	20	___ ___ ___
2481	Plainfield Pullman, yellow, 1950	100	225	___ ___ ___
2482	Westfield Pullman, yellow, 1950	100	225	___ ___ ___
2483	Livingston Obs., yellow, 1950	90	200	___ ___ ___
2521	President McKinley Obs., 62-66	40	80	___ ___ ___
2522	President Harrison V. D., 62-66	40	80	___ ___ ___
2523	President Garfield Pull., 1962-66	40	80	___ ___ ___
2530	R E A Baggage, 1954-60			
(A)	Large doors	125	375	___ ___ ___
(B)	Small doors	50	100	___ ___ ___
2531	Silver Dawn Observation, 52-60	30	70	___ ___ ___
2532	Silver Range Vista Dome, 52-60	30	70	___ ___ ___
2533	Silver Cloud Pullman, 1952-59	30	70	___ ___ ___
2534	Silver Bluff Pullman, 1952-59	30	70	___ ___ ___
2541	Alexander Hamilton Obs., 55-56*	70	190	___ ___ ___
2542	Betsy Ross Vista Dome, 1955-56*	70	190	___ ___ ___
2543	William Penn Pullman, 1955-56*	70	190	___ ___ ___
2544	Molly Pitcher Pullman, 1955-56*	70	190	___ ___ ___
2550	B & O RDC Baggage Mail Car, 1957-58	250	550	
2551	Banff Park Observation, 1957*	100	225	
2552	Skyline 500 Vista Dome, 1957*	100	225	
2553	Blair Manor Pullman, 1957*	150	325	
2554	Craig Manor Pullman, 1957*	150	325	
2555	Sunoco 1-D Tank Car, 1946-48	12	35	
2559	B & O RDC Pass. Car, 1957-58	200	325	
2560	L L Crane, 8-wheel, 1946-47	20	60	
2561	Vista Valley Obs., 1959-61*	95	225	
2562	Regal Pass Vista Dome, 59-61*	125	300	
2563	Indian Falls Pullman, 1959-61*	100	300	
2625	Madison Pullman, 1946-47*	75	250	___ ___ ___
2625	Manhattan Pullman, 1946-47*	75	250	___ ___ ___
2625	Irvington Pullman, 1946-50*			
(A)	No silhouettes	75	250	___ ___ ___
(B)	With silhouettes	75	250	___ ___ ___
2627	Madison Pullman, 1948-50*			
(A)	No silhouettes	75	225	___ ___ ___
(B)	With silhouettes	75	250	___ ___ ___
2628	Manhattan Pullman, 1948-50*			
(A)	No silhouettes	75	225	___ ___ ___
(B)	With silhouettes	75	250	___ ___ ___
2671	T C A Tender, 1968 (Like New price)	—	75	___ ___ ___
2755	S U N X 1-D Tank Car, 1945	40	150	___ ___ ___
2855	S U N X 1-D Tank Car, 1946-47	50	175	___ ___ ___
2856	B & O Scale Hopper Car, 1946-47			Not Manufactured

		Good	Exc	ColorCond $
2857	N Y C Scale Caboose, 1946			Not Manufacture
X2954	Penn Scale Boxcar, 1941-42	150	300	___ ___ ___
2955	S U N X 1-D Scale Tank, 1940-42, 1946	110	275	___ ___ ___
2956	B & O Scale Hopper Car, 40-42	150	325	___ ___ ___
2957	N Y C Scale Caboose, 1946	70	250	___ ___ ___
(3309)	Turbo Missile Launch Car, 1963-64			
(A)	Red body	20	50	___ ___ ___
(B)	Olive body	60	275	___ ___ ___
3330	Flatcar with Submarine Kit, 60-62	35	120	___ ___ ___
3330-100	Oper. Submarine Kit, 60-61	25	100	___ ___ ___
(3349)	Turbo Missile Launch Car, 62-65	20	50	___ ___ ___
3356	Operating Horse Car only, 1956-60, 1964-66	20	45	___ ___ ___
3356	Operating Horse Corral set, 1956-60, 1964-66	45	95	___ ___ ___
3356-100	Nine Black Horses, 1956-59	5	10	___ ___ ___
3356-150	Horse Car Corral	25	75	___ ___ ___
3357	Hydraulic Maintenance Car, 62-64	15	45	___ ___ ___
3359	L L Two-bin Dump, 1955-58	10	35	___ ___ ___
3360	Operating Burro Crane, 1956-57	150	300	___ ___ ___
3361	Oper. Log Dump Car, 1955-58	10	25	___ ___ ___
3362	Flatcar w/helium Tanks, 1961-63	10	35	___ ___ ___
3364	Log Dump Car, 1965-69	15	45	___ ___ ___
3366	Circus Car Corral Set, 1959-62	90	175	___ ___ ___
3366	Circus Car only, 1959-62	45	70	___ ___ ___
3366-100	(9) White Horses, 1959-60	10	25	___ ___ ___
3370	W & A Outlaw Car, 1961-64	15	40	___ ___ ___
3376	Bronx Zoo Car, 1960-6, 1969			
(A)	Blue with white lettering	15	40	___ ___ ___
(B)	Green with yellow lettering	35	100	___ ___ ___
(C)	Blue with yellow lettering	100	300	___ ___ ___
3386	Bronx Zoo Car, 1960	20	60	___ ___ ___
3409	Helicopter Car, 1961	50	125	___ ___ ___
3410	Helicopter Car, 1961-63	30	90	___ ___ ___
(3413)	Mercury Capsule Car, 1962-64	40	110	___ ___ ___
3419	Helicopter Car, 1959-65	30	110	___ ___ ___
3424	Wabash Operating Boxcar, 1956-58			
(A)	Medium blue body	25	60	___ ___ ___
(B)	Dark blue body	25	60	___ ___ ___
3424-100	Low Bridge Signal Set	10	25	___ ___ ___
3428	U. S. Mail Oper. Boxcar, 1959-60	25	75	___ ___ ___
3429	U S M C Helicopter Car, 1960	100	375	___ ___ ___
3434	Poultry Dispatch, 59-60, 64-66	30	100	___ ___ ___
3435	Traveling Aquarium Car, 1959-62			
(A)	Gold circle	250	800	___ ___ ___
(B)	Tank 1, Tank 2	100	400	___ ___ ___
(C)	Gold letter	75	150	___ ___ ___

		Good	Exc	ColorCond $
(D)	Yellow rubber stamp	50	100	___ ___ ___
3444	Erie Operating Gondola, 1957-59	25	50	___ ___ ___
3451	Oper. Log Dump Car, 1946-48	10	40	___ ___ ___
3454	P R R Oper. Merch. Car, 1946-47			
(A)	Red lettering	NRS	NRS	___ ___ ___
(B)	Blue lettering	35	100	___ ___ ___
3456	N & W Oper. Hopper, 1950-55	15	40	___ ___ ___
3459	L L Operating Dump Car, 1946-48			
(A)	Aluminum bin	75	200	___ ___ ___
(B)	Black bin	10	35	___ ___ ___
(C)	Green bin	20	50	___ ___ ___
3460	Flatcar with trailers, 1955-57	20	45	___ ___ ___
3461	Lionel Oper. Log Car, 1949-55	10	40	___ ___ ___
3462	Automatic Milk Car, 1947-48	20	40	___ ___ ___
3462P	Milk Car Platform	5	15	___ ___ ___
X3464	A T & S F Oper. Box., 1949-52	10	25	___ ___ ___
X3464	N Y C Oper. Boxcar, 1949-52	10	25	___ ___ ___
3469	L L Oper. Dump Car, 1949-55	10	35	___ ___ ___
3470	Target Launcher, 1962-64	20	60	___ ___ ___
3472	Automatic Milk Car, 1949-53	20	40	___ ___ ___
3474	Western Pacific Boxcar, 1952-53	15	50	___ ___ ___
3482	Automatic Milk Car, 1954-55	15	45	___ ___ ___
3484	Pennsylvania Oper. Boxcar, 1953	15	50	___ ___ ___
3484-25	A T & S F Oper. Boxcar, 54	20	90	___ ___ ___
3494-1	N Y C Pacemaker Boxcar, 55	20	90	___ ___ ___
3494-150	M P Operating Boxcar, 1956	45	125	___ ___ ___
3494-275	St. of Maine Oper. Box., 56-58	40	75	___ ___ ___
3494-550	Monon Oper. Box., 1957-58	100	275	___ ___ ___
3494-625	SOO Oper. Boxcar, 57-58	100	275	___ ___ ___
3509	Satellite Car, 1961	25	75	___ ___ ___
(3510)	Satellite Car, 1962	30	125	___ ___ ___
3512	Ladder Co. Car, 1959-61			
(A)	Black rooftop ladder	25	70	___ ___ ___
(B)	Silver rooftop ladder	35	125	___ ___ ___
3519	Satellite Car, 1961-64	15	50	___ ___ ___
3520	Searchlight Car, die-cast, 1952-53	30	55	___ ___ ___
3530	G M Electro Mobile Pow., 56-58	30	70	___ ___ ___
(A)	Long white stripe	40	80	___ ___ ___
(B)	Short white stripe	30	70	___ ___ ___
3530-50	Searchlight w/pole and base	10	25	___ ___ ___
3535	A E C Security Car, 1960-61	20	90	___ ___ ___
3540	Operating Radar Car, 1959-60	40	125	___ ___ ___
3545	Lionel TV Car, 1961-62	40	125	___ ___ ___
3559	Oper. Coal Dump Car, 1946-48	10	20	___ ___ ___
3562-1	A T & S F Black Operating, Barrel Car, 1954	60	150	___ ___ ___
3562-25	A T & S F Oper. Barrel Car, gray, 1954			
(A)	Red lettering	100	300	___ ___ ___

		Good	Exc	ColorCond $
(B)	Blue lettering	15	35	
3562-50	A T & S F Oper. Barrel Car, yel., 1955-56			
(A)	Painted	25	55	
(B)	Unpainted	15	35	
3562-75	A T & S F Operating Barrel Car,			
	1957-58	20	50	
3619	Helicopter Boxcar, 1962-64			
(A)	Light Yellow	30	75	
(B)	Dark Yellow	40	110	
3620	Searchlight Car, 1954-56	25	50	
3650	Extension Searchlight Car, 1956-59			
(A)	Light gray	25	60	
(B)	Dark gray	75	125	
3656	Armour Operating Cattle Car, 1949-55			
(A)	Black letters, Armour sticker	50	150	
(B)	White letters, Armour sticker	30	60	
(C)	White lettering	20	40	
3656	Stockyard with cattle	15	50	
3662	Auto. Milk Car, 1955-60, 64-66	30	60	
3665	Minuteman Operating Car, 1961-64			
(A)	Medium blue roof	75	150	
(B)	Dark blue roof	20	45	
3666	Minuteman Boxcar			
	with missile, 1964	150	500	
3672	Bosco Operating Boxcar, 1959-60			
(A)	With "Bosco" decal	110	425	
(B)	Without "Bosco" decal	110	425	
3820	Flatcar with Submarine, 1960-62	30	180	
3830	Flatcar with Submarine, 1960-63	30	90	
3854	Oper. Merchandise Car, 1946-47	200	500	
3927	L L Track Cleaner, 1956-60	60	110	
3927-50	Track Cleaning Fluid, 1957-69	.50	2	
3927-75	Track Cleaning Pads, 1957-69	.50	2	
4357	Penn N5 Cab., electronic, 48-49	50	150	
4452	Penn Gondola, electronic, 46-49	30	75	
4454	Baby Ruth P R R Boxcar,			
	electronic, 1946-49	50	150	
4457	Penn N5 Cab., electr., 1946-47	40	140	
4681	Steam 6-8-6, electronic, 1950			Not Manufactured
4776-18	(See 2472, 2457)			
4810	S P Trainmaster, prototype, 54	NRS	NRS	
5159	Maintenance Kit, 1963-65	1	3	
5159-50	Maint. and Lube Kit, 1966-69	1	3	
5160	Viewing Stand	50	100	
5364 17	(See 6417)			
5459	L L Dump Car, electronic, 46-49	30	70	
6002	N Y C Gondola, 1950	4	10	
X6004	Baby Ruth P R R Boxcar, 1950	2	5	

		Good	Exc	ColorCond $
6007	L L SP Type Caboose, 1950	2	5	_____
6009	R.C. Uncoupling Track, 1953-54	—	8	_____
6012	Lionel Gondola, 1951-56	2	5	_____
6014	Airex Boxcar, 1960, uncat.	20	45	_____
6014	Bosco P R R Boxcar, 1958			
(A)	White body	25	50	_____
(B)	Red or orange body	4	9	_____
6014	Chun King Boxcar, 1957, uncat.	60	115	_____
6014	Frisco Boxcar, 1957, 1963-69			
(A)	White body	3	7	_____
(B)	Red body	3	7	_____
(C)	White w/coin slot	20	40	_____
(D)	Orange body	5	12	_____
X6014	Baby Ruth P R R Boxcar			
(A)	White body	2	4	_____
(B)	Red body	2	4	_____
6014-150	Wix Boxcar, 1959, uncat.	75	150	_____
6015	Sunoco 1-D Tank Car (O27), 1954-55			
(A)	Painted tank	15	30	_____
(B)	Unpainted tank	3	7	_____
6017	L L SP Type Cab. (O27), 1951-62	2	5	_____
6017	SP Type Cab. Lionel, 1956 only	2	4	_____
6017-50	U S M C SP Type Cab. 1958	20	50	_____
6017-100	B & M SP Type Caboose, 1959, 1962, 1965-66			
(A)	Purplish blue	250	700	_____
(B)	Medium or light blue	10	20	_____
6017-185	A T & S F SP Type 4 Caboose, 1959-60	10	30	_____
6017-200	U. S. Navy SP Type 4 Caboose, 1960	25	80	_____
6017-225	A T & S F SP Type 4 Caboose, circa 1963, uncatalogued	10	45	_____
6017-235	A T & S F SP Type 4 Cab., 62	20	40	_____
6019	RCS Track Set (O27), 1948-66	1	3	_____
6024	Nabisco Shredded Wheat Box., 57	10	25	_____
6024	R C A Whirlpool Boxcar (O27), 1957, uncatalogued	30	55	_____
6025	Gulf 1-D Tank Car (O27), 56-58	3	10	_____
6027	Alaska SP Type 2A Caboose, 59	25	75	_____
6029	Remote Control Uncoupling Track (O27), 1955-63	.25	1	_____
6032	Lionel Gond., black (O27), 52-54	2	5	_____
X6034	Baby Ruth P R R Boxcar (O27), 1953-54	5	12	_____
6035	Sunoco 1-D Tank Car (O27), 1952-53	2	5	_____
6037	L L Caboose SP Type 3A (O27), 1952-54	2	4	_____

		Good	Exc	Color	Cond	$
6042	Lionel Gon. (O27), 1959-61, 62-64, uncat.					
(A)	Blue body	2	5			
(B)	Black body	2	5			
6044	Airex Boxcar (O27), orange lettering					
(A)	Medium blue	5	12			
(B)	Teal blue	40	80			
(C)	Dark blue/purple	70	250			
6044-1X	Nestles/McCall's Boxcar (no lettering), circa 1962-63	400	750			
6045	L L 2-D Tank Car, 59-64, uncat.	15	25			
6045	Cities Service 2-D Tank, 60, uncat.	10	20			
6047	L L SP Type 2A/4 Cab., 1962	2	4			
6050	Lionel Savings Bank Boxcar, 1961	9	18			
6050	Swift Refrigerator, 1962-63	10	20			
6050	Libby's Boxcar, 1963					
(A)	Green stems	12	20			
(B)	No green stems	50	100			
6057	L L SP Type 1A/4 Cab., 1959-62	2	4			
6057-50	L L or. SP Type 4 Cab., 62	15	25			
6058	C & O SP Type Caboose, 1961	10	45			
6059	M St L SP Type 4 Caboose, 1961-69					
(A)	Painted red	5	10			
(B)	Unpainted red	3	8			
(C)	Unpainted maroon	5	10			
6062	N Y C Gondola, with cable reels, 1959-62	5	15			
6062-50	N Y C Gon., w/2 canisters, 69	5	15			
(6067)	Caboose (no lett.), SP Type, 62	2	4			
6076	A T S F Hopper, 1963, uncat.	9	20			
6076	LV Hop., gray (no lett.), 1961-63	5	9			
6076-75	L V Hopper Car, 1963	5	9			
6076-100	Hopper Car (no lett.), 1963	10	20			
6109	Flatcar with logs, gray, 1952	35	45			
6110	Steam 2-4-2, 6001T Tdr. 1950-51	10	25			
(6111)	Flatcar with logs, 1955-57	5	15			
6112	Lionel Gondola, 1956-58					
(A)	Black body	3	8			
(B)	Blue body	3	8			
(C)	White body	4	14			
6119	D L & W Work Cab., red, 55-56	10	25			
6119-25	D L & W Work Caboose, orange, 1956-59	10	25			
6119-50	D L & W Cab., brown, 1956	10	35			
6119-75	D L & W Caboose, gray, 1957	10	25			
6119-100	D L & W Work Caboose, red/gray 1957-66, 1969	8	18			
(6119-125)	Work Caboose (no lettering), olive drab, c. 1960	NRS	NRS			

		Good	Exc	ColorCond $
(6120)	Work Caboose (no lettering), yellow, 1961-62	7	20	___ ___ ___
(6121)	Flatcar with pipes, 1956-57	5	15	___ ___ ___
6130	A T & S F Work Caboose, 1961, 1965-69	10	30	___ ___ ___
6139	R.C. Uncoupling Track (O27), 1963			
6142	Lionel Gondola, 1963-66	2	5	___ ___ ___
6142-50	Lionel Gon., green, 61-63, 66	5	10	___ ___ ___
6142-75	Lionel Gondola, blue, 1961-63	2	5	___ ___ ___
6142-100	Lionel Gon., green, 1964-65	2	5	___ ___ ___
6142-150	Lionel Gon., blue, c. 1961-63	2	5	___ ___ ___
6142-175	Lionel Gondola, c. 1961-63	2	5	___ ___ ___
6149	Remote Control Uncoupling Track (O27), 1964-69	.25	1	___ ___ ___
(6151)	Flatcar with Patrol Truck, 1958	20	60	___ ___ ___
6162	N Y C Gondola, 1959-68			
(A)	Blue body	3	7	___ ___ ___
(B)	Red body	25	75	___ ___ ___
6162-60	Alaska Gondola, 1959	20	40	___ ___ ___
6167	L L SP Type 4 Caboose, 1963	3	7	___ ___ ___
6167-85	U P SP Type 4 Caboose, 1969	10	25	___ ___ ___
6175	Flatcar with rocket, 1958-61	25	60	___ ___ ___
6176	L V Hopper, 1964-66, 1969	3	7	___ ___ ___
(6176)	Hopper (no lettering), yellow	10	20	___ ___ ___
6219	C & O Work Caboose, 1960	20	65	___ ___ ___
6220	S F NW-2 Switcher, 1949-50	100	275	___ ___ ___
6250	Seaboard NW-2 Switcher, 1954-55			
(A)	Decals	125	300	___ ___ ___
(B)	Rubber stamped	100	275	___ ___ ___
6257	Lionel SP Type Caboose, 1948-56, 1963-64	2	4	___ ___ ___
6257X	Lionel Lines Caboose	10	25	___ ___ ___
6257-25	Lionel SP Type 3A Caboose	2	4	___ ___ ___
6257-50	Lionel SP Type 1 or 3A Cab.	2	4	___ ___ ___
6257-100	Lionel SP Type 4 Caboose	5	15	___ ___ ___
6262	Flatcar with wheels, 1956-57			
(A)	1956-57, black	15	40	___ ___ ___
(B)	1956, red	50	400	___ ___ ___
6264	Flatcar with lumber for forklift set, 57-60	20	45	___ ___ ___
6311	Flatcar with three pipes, 1955	15	40	___ ___ ___
6315	Gulf 1-D Chemical Tank Car, 1956-59, 1968-69			
(A)	Early painted	20	40	___ ___ ___
(B)	Late unpainted	25	55	___ ___ ___
(C)	Late unpainted w/built date	NRS	NRS	___ ___ ___
6315	L L 1-D Tank Car, 1963-66	10	25	___ ___ ___
6342	N Y C Gondola, 1956-58, 64-66	7	25	___ ___ ___

		Good	Exc	Color	Cond	$
6343	Barrel Ramp Car, 1961-62	15	35			
6346	Alcoa Quad Hopper, 1956	20	45			
6352	P F E Reefer from 352 Icing Depot, 1955-57	25	65			
6356	N Y C Stock Car, 2 level, 54-55	10	35			
6357	Lionel SP Type Caboose, 1948-61	6	15			
6357-50	A T & S F SP Type 4 Cab.	250	900			
6361	Flatcar w/timber, 1960-61, 64-69	20	55			
6362	Truck Car with three trucks, 1955-56					
(A)	Shiny orange	10	30			
(B)	Dull orange	50	100			
6376	L L Circus Stock Car, 1956-57	20	50			
(6401)	Flatcar	3	15			
(6402)	Flatcar with reels or boat, 1962, 1964-66, 1969	4	8			
6404	Brown Flatcar w/brown auto, 60	—	250			
6405	Maroon Flatcar with trailer, 1961	10	30			
(6406)	Flatcar with yellow auto, 1961	25	75			
(6407)	Flatcar with rocket, 1963	75	450			
(6408)	Flatcar with pipes, 1963	15	30			
6409	Flatcar with pipes, 1963	15	30			
6411	Flatcar with logs, 1948-50	10	30			
6413	Mercury Project Car, 1962-63	30	150			
6414	Evans Auto Loader, 1955-66					
(A)	Early premium cars with windows, chrome bumpers, and rubber tires; red, yellow, blue, and white	20	60			
(B)	Four cheap cars, without trim, two red, two yellow	—	450			
(C)	Four red cars w/gray bumpers	50	175			
(D)	Four yellow cars w/gray bumpers	—	450			
(E)	Four brown cars w/gray bumpers	300	700			
(F)	Four green cars w/gray bumpers	400	1000			
6415	Sunoco 3-D Tank Car, 1953-55, 1964-66, 1969	5	20			
6416	Boat Loader Car, 1961-63	75	150			
6417	Pennsylvania Porthole Caboose, 1953-57					
(A)	W/ "NEW YORK ZONE"	10	25			
(b)	W/o "NEW YORK ZONE"	80	225			
6417-3	(See 6417-25)					
6417-25	L L N5C Caboose, 1954	15	40			
6417-50	L V N5C Caboose, 1954					
(A)	Tuscan	300	1000			
(B)	Gray	30	100			
6417-51	(See 6417-50)					
6417-53	(See 6417-25)					
6418	Bridge, metal base, plastic sides	5	15			
6418	Flatcar with steel girders, 1955-57	30	65			

	Good	Exc	ColorCond $
6419 D L & W Work Caboose, early frame 1948-50, 1952-57	10	25	___ ___ ___
6419-25 D L & W Work Cab., 1954-55	10	30	___ ___ ___
6419-50 D L & W Work Caboose, late frame 1956-57	15	35	___ ___ ___
6419-57 (See 6419-100)			
6419-75 D L & W Work Caboose, late frame 1956-57	10	30	___ ___ ___
6419-100 N & W Work Cab., 1957-58	40	100	___ ___ ___
6420 D L & W Work Caboose, with light, 1948-50	30	85	___ ___ ___
6424 Flatcar with two autos, 1956-59	15	35	___ ___ ___
6425 Gulf 3-D Tank Car, 1956-58	10	30	___ ___ ___
6427 Lionel Lines N5C Caboose, 54-60	10	25	___ ___ ___
6427-(60) Virginian N5C Caboose, 58	90	300	___ ___ ___
6427-500 P R R N5C Girls Caboose, 1957-58*	100	350	___ ___ ___
6428 U S Mail Boxcar, 1960-61, 65-66	10	35	___ ___ ___
6429 D L & W Work Caboose, AAR trucks, 1963	100	300	___ ___ ___
6430 Flat. w/Cooper-Jarrett vans, 56-58	20	50	___ ___ ___
6431 Flatcar with vans, 1966	40	225	___ ___ ___
6434 Poultry Dispatch, 1958-59	30	60	___ ___ ___
6436-1 L V Quad Hopper, black, 1955	10	35	___ ___ ___
6436-25 L V Quad Hop., maroon, 55-57	10	35	___ ___ ___
6436-57 (See 6436-500)			
6436-110 L V Quad Hopper, 1963-68			
(A) Without cover	15	35	___ ___ ___
(B) With cover and "NEW 3-55"	75	150	___ ___ ___
6436-500 L V Girls Hopper, lilac, "643657", 1957-58*	75	200	___ ___ ___
6436-1969 T C A Quad Hopper, 1969	—	125	___ ___ ___
6437 Penn N5C Caboose, 1961-68	10	25	___ ___ ___
6440 Flatcar with vans, 1961-63	25	75	___ ___ ___
6440 Green Pullman, 1948-49	20	40	___ ___ ___
6441 Green Observation, 1948-49	20	40	___ ___ ___
6442 Brown Pullman, 1949	25	60	___ ___ ___
6443 Brown Observation, 1949	25	60	___ ___ ___
6445 Fort Knox Gold Reserve, 1961-63	40	100	___ ___ ___
6446 N & W Quad "546446", 1954-55	15	45	___ ___ ___
6446-25 N & W Quad "644625", 55-57	15	35	___ ___ ___
6446-60 (See 6436-110(B))			
6447 Pennsylvania N5C Caboose, 63	100	350	___ ___ ___
6448 Target Car, 1961-64	10	20	___ ___ ___
6452 P R R Gondola, black, 1948-49	5	12	___ ___ ___
X6454(A) Baby Ruth P R R Box., 48	50	200	___ ___ ___
X6454(B) N Y C Boxcar, orange, 48	40	150	___ ___ ___
X6454(C) N Y C Boxcar, brown, 48	20	50	___ ___ ___

		Good	Exc	ColorCond $
X6454(D)	N Y C Boxcar, tan, 1948	10	30	___ ___ ___
X6454(E)	A T & S F Boxcar, 1948	10	30	___ ___ ___
X6454(F)	S P Boxcar, 1949	25	75	___ ___ ___
X6454(G)	S P Boxcar, 1950	15	40	___ ___ ___
X6454(H)	S P Boxcar, 1951-52	20	50	___ ___ ___
X6454(J)	Erie Boxcar, 1949-52	20	50	___ ___ ___
X6454(K)	Pennsylvania Boxcar, 49-52	20	50	___ ___ ___
6456	Lehigh Valley Short Hopper, 1948-55			
(A)	Black	5	9	___ ___ ___
(B)	Maroon	5	9	___ ___ ___
(C)	Enamel red, yellow lettering	50	100	___ ___ ___
(D)	Enamel red, white lettering	150	500	___ ___ ___
6457	Lionel SP Type, 1949-52	10	25	___ ___ ___
6460	Bucyrus Erie black cab Crane, 8-wheel, 1952-54	25	60	___ ___ ___
6460-25	Bucyrus Erie red cab Crane, 8-wheel, with box, 1954	40	80	___ ___ ___
6461	Transformer Car, 1949-50	25	75	___ ___ ___
6462	N Y C Gondola, black, 1949-54	3	9	___ ___ ___
6462	N Y C Gondola, green, 1954-56	3	9	___ ___ ___
6462	N Y C Gon., red, 1950-52, 54-57	2	8	___ ___ ___
6462-500	N Y C Gon., pink, 1957-58*	50	150	___ ___ ___
6463	Rocket Fuel 2-D Tank, 1962-63	10	25	___ ___ ___
6464-1	W P Boxcar, 1953-54			
(A)	Blue lettering	25	75	___ ___ ___
(B)	Red lettering	300	1200	___ ___ ___
6464-25	G N Boxcar, orange, 1953-54	20	50	___ ___ ___
6464-50	M & St L Box., tuscan, 53-56	20	50	___ ___ ___
6464-75	Rock Island Boxcar, 53-54, 69	25	75	___ ___ ___
6464-100	W P Boxcar, 1954-55			
(A)	Long yellow feather	30	100	___ ___ ___
(B)	Short yellow feather, silver body and door paint	100	225	___ ___ ___
(C)	Orange body, lighter blue feather	250	600	___ ___ ___
(D)	Dark orange body, blue feather	300	750	___ ___ ___
6464-125	N Y C Boxcar, 1954-56	30	100	___ ___ ___
6464-150	M P Boxcar, 1954-55, 1957	25	110	___ ___ ___
6464-175	Rock Island Boxcar, 1954-55			
(A)	Blue lettering	25	100	___ ___ ___
(B)	Black lettering	300	900	___ ___ ___
6464-200	P R R Boxcar, 1954-55, 69	40	125	___ ___ ___
6464-225	S P Boxcar, 1954-56	35	100	___ ___ ___
6464-250	W P Boxcar, 1966	40	100	___ ___ ___
6464-275	State of Maine Boxcar, 1955, 1957-59			
(A)	Striped doors	20	75	___ ___ ___
(B)	Solid doors	40	125	___ ___ ___
6464-300	Rutland Boxcar, 1955-56			
(A)	Rubber stamped	30	90	___ ___ ___

		Good	Exc	Color	Cond	$
(B)	Split door	300	750	___	___	___
(C)	Solid shield	750	2000	___	___	___
(D)	Heat stamped	50	150	___	___	___
6464-325	B & O Sentinel Boxcar, 56	150	450	___	___	___
6464-350	M K T Katy Boxcar, 1956	80	200	___	___	___
6464-375	Central of Georgia Boxcar, 1956-57, 1966	30	90	___	___	___
6464-400	B & O Timesaver Boxcar, 1956-57, 1969	20	75	___	___	___
6464-425	N H Boxcar, 1956-58	20	40	___	___	___
6464-450	G N Boxcar, 1956-57, 1966	30	90	___	___	___
6464-475	B & M Boxcar, 1957-60, 1965-66, 1968	12	35	___	___	___
6464-500	Timken Boxcar, 1957-58, 1969					
(A)	Yellow and white w/charcoal lett.	50	125	___	___	___
(B)	Yellow and white with red heat-stamped lettering	—	1200	___	___	___
(C)	Green, white, gold, or red heat-stamped lettering	—	550	___	___	___
(D)	"BLT 1-71 BY LIONEL MPC"	30	110	___	___	___
(E)	"9200" on end numberboards and "BLT 1-71 BY LIONEL MPC"	120	250	___	___	___
6464-510	N Y C Pacemaker Boxcar, 1957-58	150	450	___	___	___
6464-515	M K T Boxcar, 1957-58	150	450	___	___	___
6464-525	M & St L Boxcar, 1957-58, 1964-66					
(A)	Painted yellow body	25	90	___	___	___
(B)	Unpainted yellow body	50	125	___	___	___
(C)	Painted yellow body and roof	500	1000	___	___	___
6464-650	D & R G W Box., 57-58, 66	25	90	___	___	___
6464-700	S F Boxcar, 1961, 1966	20	100	___	___	___
6464-725	N H Boxcar, 1962-66, 1968					
(A)	Orange body	20	50	___	___	___
(B)	Black body	50	175	___	___	___
6464-825	Alaska Boxcar, 1959-60	100	150	___	___	___
6464-900	N Y C Boxcar, 1960-66	25	90	___	___	___
6464-1965	T C A Pittsburgh Box., 65	—	250	___	___	___
6464-1970	See 1970-89	—	110	___	___	___
6464-1971	See 1970-89	—	175	___	___	___
6465	Sunoco 2-D Tank Car, 1948-56	3	10	___	___	___
6465	Cities Service 2-D Tank, 1960-62	10	20	___	___	___
6465	Gulf 2-D Tank Car, 1958					
(A)	Black tank	25	75	___	___	___
(B)	Gray tank	10	20	___	___	___
6465	L L 2-D Tank Car, 1959, 1963-64					
(A)	Black tank	10	20	___	___	___
(B)	Orange tank	3	10	___	___	___
6467	Bulkhead Flatcar, 1956	20	50	___	___	___

		Good	Exc	ColorCond $
6468	B & O Auto Boxcar, 1953-55			
(A)	Tuscan	100	300	___ ___ ___
(B)	Blue	20	45	___ ___ ___
6468-25	N H Auto Boxcar, 1956-58	15	65	___ ___ ___
(6469)	Lionel Liquified Gases Car, 63	30	150	___ ___ ___
6470	Explosives Car, 1959-60	10	30	___ ___ ___
6472	Refrigerator Car, 1950-53	10	20	___ ___ ___
6473	Horse Transport Car, 1962-69	10	20	___ ___ ___
6475	Heinz 57 Vat Car, post-factory alteration	50	100	___ ___ ___
6475	Libby's Crushed Pineapple Vat Car, 1963, uncatalogued	15	40	___ ___ ___
6475	Pickles Vat Car, 1960-62	15	40	___ ___ ___
6476	L V Hopper, 1957-69	5	9	___ ___ ___
6476-1	L V Hopper, gray, T T O S, 1969	25	75	___ ___ ___
6476-135	L V Hopper, yellow, 1964-66, 1968	5	9	___ ___ ___
6476-160	L V Hopper, black, 1969	5	9	___ ___ ___
6476-185	L V Hopper, yellow, 1969	5	9	___ ___ ___
6477	Bulkhead Car w/pipes, 1957-58	15	50	___ ___ ___
6480	Explosives Car, red, 1961	10	30	___ ___ ___
6482	Refrigerator Car, 1957	20	50	___ ___ ___
(6500)	Flat. w/Bonanza plane, 62, 65	250	400	___ ___ ___
(6501)	Flatcar with jet boat, 1962-63	25	100	___ ___ ___
(6502)	Flatcar w/bridge girder, 1962	15	45	___ ___ ___
6511	Flatcar with pipes, 1953-56	10	40	___ ___ ___
(6512)	Cherry Picker Car, 1962-63	30	80	___ ___ ___
6517	L L Bay Window Caboose, 1955-59			
(A)	Underscored	25	60	___ ___ ___
(B)	Not underscored	20	50	___ ___ ___
6517-75	Erie B/W Caboose, 1966	150	350	___ ___ ___
6517-1966	T C A B/W Caboose, 1966	60	220	___ ___ ___
6518	Transformer Car, 1956-58	25	90	___ ___ ___
6519	Allis Chalmers Flatcar, 1958-61			
(A)	Dark/medium orange base	25	55	___ ___ ___
(B)	Dull light orange base	40	90	___ ___ ___
6520	Searchlight Car, 1949-51			
(A)	Tan diesel generator	150	450	___ ___ ___
(B)	Green diesel generator	75	225	___ ___ ___
(C)	Maroon or orange diesel gen.	25	55	___ ___ ___
6530	Fire Fighting Car, red, 1960-62	25	60	___ ___ ___
6530	Fire Fighting Car, black, 1960-61	—	750	___ ___ ___
6536	M & St L Quad Hop., 58-59, 63	15	40	___ ___ ___
6544	Missile Firing Car, 1960-64			
(A)	White-lettered console	25	125	___ ___ ___
(B)	Black-lettered console	100	350	___ ___ ___
6555	Sunoco 1-D Tank Car, 1949-50	15	45	___ ___ ___

		Good	Exc	Color	Cond	$
6556	M K T Stock Car, 1958	60	200	___	___	___
6557	Lionel SP Type Caboose, smoke, 1958-59	75	225	___	___	___
6560	Bucyrus Erie Crane w/stack, 8-wheel, 1955-58, 1968-69					
(A)	Reddish-orange or black cab, early construction	60	160	___	___	___
(B)	Gray cab	40	80	___	___	___
(C)	Red cab	20	50	___	___	___
(D)	Dark blue (Hagerstown)	35	85	___	___	___
6560-25	Bucyrus Erie Crane, 8-whl., 56	40	105	___	___	___
6561	Reel Car, 1953-56	20	60	___	___	___
6562	N Y C Gondola with canisters, 1956-58	7	25	___	___	___
6572	R E A Refrig. Car, 1958-59, 63	25	75	___	___	___
6630	I R B M Rocket Launcher, 1961, uncatalogued	20	75	___	___	___
6636	Alaska Quad Hopper, 1959-60	17	40	___	___	___
6640	U S M C Rocket Launcher, 1960	75	225	___	___	___
6646	Lionel Lines Stock Car, 1957	10	30	___	___	___
6650	I R B M Rocket Launcher, 59-63	20	45	___	___	___
6650-80	Missile Car, 1960	1	4	___	___	___
6651	U S M C Cannon Car, 64, uncat.	40	100	___	___	___
6656	Lionel Lines Stock Car, 1949-55	5	15	___	___	___
6657	Rio Grande SP Type Cab., 57-58	50	125	___	___	___
6660	Flatcar with crane, 1958	20	65	___	___	___
6670	Flatcar with crane, 1959-60	20	50	___	___	___
6672	S F Refrigerator Car, 1954-56					
(A)	Blue lettering, two lines	20	50	___	___	___
(B)	Black lettering, two lines	20	50	___	___	___
(C)	Blue lettering, three lines	60	250	___	___	___
6736	Detroit & Mack. Quad, 1960-62	17	35	___	___	___
6763-85	Lehigh Valley Hopper	5	9	___	___	___
6800	Flatcar with airplane, 1957-60	75	150	___	___	___
6801	Flatcar with boat, 1957-60	20	50	___	___	___
6802	Flatcar with bridge, 1958-59	10	25	___	___	___
6803	Flatcar w/tank and truck, 58-59	50	125	___	___	___
6804	Flatcar w/U S M C trucks, 58-59	50	125	___	___	___
6805	Atomic Disposal Flatcar, 58-59	35	100	___	___	___
6806	Flatcar w/U S M C trucks, 58-59	50	125	___	___	___
6807	Lionel Flatcar with boat, 1958-59	35	75	___	___	___
6808	Flatcar w/U S M C trucks, 58-59	50	125	___	___	___
6809	Flatcar w/U S M C trucks, 58-59	50	125	___	___	___
6810	Flatcar with trailer, 1958	15	35	___	___	___
6812	Track Maintenance Car, 1959	15	75	___	___	___
6814	Lionel Medical Caboose, 1959-61	30	125	___	___	___
6816	Flatcar with bulldozer, 1959-60					
(A)	Red car	75	275	___	___	___
(B)	Black car	200	600	___	___	___

	Good	Exc	Color	Cond	$
6816-100 Allis Chalmers Tractor, 59-60	50	150			
6817 Flatcar with scraper, 1959-60					
(A) Black	300	900			
(B) Red	100	300			
6817-100 Allis Chalmers Scraper, 59-60	75	200			
6818 Transformer Car, 1958	10	40			
6819 Flatcar with helicopter, 1959-60	25	75			
6820 Flatcar with missile transport helicopter, 1960-61					
(A) Light blue-painted flatcar	60	225			
(B) Darker blue flatcar	40	150			
6821 Flatcar with Crates, 1959-60	10	20			
6822 Searchlight Car, 1961-69	20	50			
6823 Flatcar w/I R B M missiles, 59-60	20	65			
6824 U S M C Work Caboose, 1960	50	160			
(6824) Rescue Unit Work Caboose, c. 1964, uncatalogued	50	125			
6825 Flatcar with bridge, 1959-62	15	45			
6826 Flatcar with trees, 1959-60	30	110			
6827 Flatcar w/steam shovel, 1960-63	40	75			
6827-100 Harnischfeger Shovel, 1960	25	75			
6828 Flatcar w/crane, 1960-63, 1966	40	100			
6828-100 Harnischfeger Crane, 1960	25	75			
6830 Flatcar w/submarine, 1960-61	40	90			
6844 Flatcar with missiles, 1959-60					
(A) Black plastic flatcar	20	60			
(B) Red plastic flatcar	300	700			
63132 (See 3464)					
64173 (See 6427 Lionel)					
65400 (See 2454 or 6454)					
81000 (See 6417 PRR)					
96743 (See 6454)					
159000 (See 3464)					
336155 (See 3361)					
477618 (See 2457 or 2472)					
536417 (See 6417 PRR)					
546446 (See 6446)					
576419 (See 6419-100)					
576427 (See 6427-500)					
641751 (See 6417-50)					
A Transformer, 90 watts, 1947-48	—	25			
CTC Lockon (O and O27), 1947-69	—	1			
ECU-1 Electronic Control Unit, 1946	20	50			
KW Transformer, 190 watts, 1950-65	—	125			
LTC Lockon (O and O27), 1950-69	—	7			
LW Transformer, 125 watts, 1955-56	—	60			
OC Curved Track (O), 1945-61	—	1.50			
OCS Curved Ins. Trk. (O), 1946-50	NRS	NRS			
OC1/2 Half Sec. Curve Trk. (O), 45-66	—	1.50			

		Good	Exc	Color	Cond	$
OS	Straight Track (O), 1945-61	—	1.50	___	___	___
OSS	Straight Insulated Track, 46-50	NRS	NRS	___	___	___
OTC	Lockon Track (O and O27)	—	5	___	___	___
Q	Transformer, 75 watts, 1946	—	15	___	___	___
R	Transformer, 110 watts, 1946-47	—	30	___	___	___
RW	Transformer, 110 watts, 1948-54	—	30	___	___	___
RCS	Remote Control Track (O), 45-48	—	10	___	___	___
SP	Smoke Pellets, bottle, 1948-69	—	10	___	___	___
SW	Transformer, 130 watts, 1961-66	—	60	___	___	___
TW	Transformer, 175 watts, 1953-60	—	75	___	___	___
TOC	Curved Trk. (O), 62-66, 68-69	—	1.50	___	___	___
TOC1/2	Half Sec. Str. Trk. (O), 62-66	—	1.50	___	___	___
TOS	Straight Track (O), 1962-69	—	1.50	___	___	___
UCS	Remote Control Track (O), 45-69	—	15	___	___	___
UTC	Lockon (O, O27, Standard), 1945	—	1.25	___	___	___
V	Transformer, 150 watts, 1946-47	—	60	___	___	___
VW	Transformer, 150 watts, 1948-49	—	125	___	___	___
Z	Transformer, 250 watts, 1945-47	—	100	___	___	___
ZW	Transformer, 250 watts, 1948-49	—	175	___	___	___
ZW	Transformer, 275 watts, 1950-66	—	200	___	___	___
No Number	SP Type Caboose (see 6167)					
No Number	Work Caboose (see 6120, 6824)					
No Number	Flatcar (see 6401, 6402, 6406)					
No Number	Gondola (see 6142)	1	2	___	___	___
No Number	Hopper (see 6176)					
No Number	Turbo Missile Car (see 3309, 3349)					
No Number	Rolling Stock (see 3413, 3510, 6111, 6121, 6151, 6407, 6408, 6409, 6469, 6500, 6501, 6502, 6512)					

		Exc	LN	Color	Cond	$
3	(See 8104)					
3	(See 8701, 8630)					
4	(See 18008)					
7-1100	Happy Huff 'n Puff, 1975	40	60			
7-1200	Gravel Gus, 1975	15	20			
7-1400	Happy Huff 'n Puff Junior, 75	40	65			
GM 50	(See 8359)					
303	L O T S Stauffer Chem. Tank, 85	—	60			
484	(See 8587)					
491	(See 7203)					
0511	T C A St. Louis Baggage, 1981	—	75			
0512	N Y C Toy Fair Reefer, 1981	125	150			
530	(See 8378)					
550C	Curved Track, 1970	.75	1.25			
550S	Straight Track, 1970	.75	1.25			
577	(See 9562)					
578	(See 9563)					
579	(See 9564)					
580	(See 9565)					
581	(See 9566)					
582	(See 9567)					
611	(See 8100)					
634	Santa Fe NW-2 Switcher, c. 1970	55	100			
659	(See 8101)					
672	(See 8610)					
779	(See 8215)					
783	(See 8406)					
784	(See 8606)					
785	(See 18002)					
1050	New Englander set, 1980-81	NRS	NRS			
1052	Chesapeake Flyer set, 1980	NRS	NRS			
1053	The James Gang set, 1980-82	220	250			
1070	The Royal Limited set, 1980	400	450			
1071	Mid Atlantic Limited set, 1980	375	430			
1072	Cross Country Express set, 1980-81	NRS	NRS			
1080	Wabash Cannonball Set, 1970	NRS	NRS			
1081	Wabash Cannonball set, 1971	NRS	NRS			
1081	Wabash Cannonball set, 1972	NRS	NRS			
1082	Yard Boss set, 1970	NRS	NRS			
1083	Pacemaker set, 1970	NRS	NRS			
1084	G T & W set, 1970	NRS	NRS			
1085	S F Exp. Diesel Freight set, 70	NRS	NRS			
1085	Santa Fe Twin Diesel set, 1971	NRS	NRS			

		Exc	LN	Color	Cond	$
1086	The Mountaineer set, 1970	Not Manufactured				
1087	Midnight Express set, 1970	Not Manufactured				
1091	Sears Special set, 1970, uncat.	NRS	NRS	___	___	___
1092	79N97081C Sears, 1970, uncat.	NRS	NRS	___	___	___
1092	79C97105C Sears 6-Unit set, 1971, uncatalogued	NRS	NRS	___	___	___
1150	L. A. S. E. R. Train set, 81-82	130	160	___	___	___
1151	U P Thunder Freight set, 81-82	NRS	NRS	___	___	___
1153	J. C. Penney Thunderball Freight set, 1981, uncatalogued	NRS	NRS	___	___	___
1154	Reading Yard King set, 81-82	NRS	NRS	___	___	___
1155	Cannonball Freight set, 1982	NRS	NRS	___	___	___
1158	Maple Leaf Limited set, 1981	500	575	___	___	___
1159	Toys 'R Us Midnight Flyer set, 1981, uncatalogued	NRS	NRS	___	___	___
T-1171	C N Steam Loco set, 1971	NRS	NRS	___	___	___
T-1172	Yardmaster set, 1971	NRS	NRS	___	___	___
T-1173	G T W set, 1971-73	NRS	NRS	___	___	___
T-1174	C N set, 1971, 1973	350	450	___	___	___
T-1174	C N set, 1972	NRS	NRS	___	___	___
1182	Yardmaster set, 1971	100	125	___	___	___
1182	Yardmaster set, 1972	NRS	NRS	___	___	___
1183	Silver Star set, 1971	NRS	NRS	___	___	___
1183	Silver Star set, 1972	NRS	NRS	___	___	___
1184	The Allegheny set, 1971	NRS	NRS	___	___	___
1186	Cross Country Express set, 71	NRS	NRS	___	___	___
1186	Cross Country Express set, 72	NRS	NRS	___	___	___
1187	Service Station set, 1971, uncat.	450	550	___	___	___
1190	Sears Special #1 set, 71, uncat.	NRS	NRS	___	___	___
1195	J. C. Penney Special set, 1971, uncatalogued	NRS	NRS	___	___	___
1198	Unnamed set, 1971, uncat.	NRS	NRS	___	___	___
1199	Ford Autolite set, 1971, uncat.	NRS	NRS	___	___	___
1223	L O T S Seattle & North Coast, Hi-cube Boxcar, 1986	—	150	___	___	___
1250	Service Station set, 1972, uncat.	NRS	NRS	___	___	___
1252	Heavy Iron set, 1982-83	NRS	NRS	___	___	___
1253	Quicksilver Express set, 82-83	325	370	___	___	___
1254	Black Cave Flyer set, 1982	70	90	___	___	___
1260	The Continental Limited, 1982	525	600	___	___	___
1261	49N95211 Sears Black Cave Flyer set, 1982, uncatalogued	NRS	NRS	___	___	___
1262	Toys 'R Us Heavy Iron set, 1982, uncatalogued	NRS	NRS	___	___	___
1263	XU671-0701A J. C. Penney Overland Freight set, 1982, uncatalogued	NRS	NRS	___	___	___
1264	Nibco Express set, 1982, uncat.	175	225	___	___	___
1265	Tappan Special set, 1982, uncat.	80	100	___	___	___

		Exc	LN	Color	Cond	$
T-1272	Yardmaster set, 1972-73	NRS	NRS			
T-1273	Silver Star set, 1972- 73	NRS	NRS			
1280	Kickapoo Valley & Northern set, 1972-73	125	175			
T-1280	Kickapoo Valley & Northern set, 1972	NRS	NRS			
1284	Allegheny set, 1972	NRS	NRS			
1285	Santa Fe Twin Diesel set, 1972	NRS	NRS			
1287	Pioneer Dockside Switcher set, 1972	NRS	NRS			
1289	(See 17875)					
1290	Sears set, 1972, uncatalogued	NRS	NRS			
1291	Sears set, 1972, uncatalogued	NRS	NRS			
1300	Gravel Gus Junior, 1975	15	20			
1346	Montgomery Ward Cross Country Express set, 1983, uncatalogued	NRS	NRS			
1349	Toys 'R Us Heavy Iron, 1983, uncatalogued	NRS	NRS			
1350	Service Station set, 1973, uncat.	NRS	NRS			
1351	Baltimore & Ohio set, 1983-84	200	225			
1352	Rocky Mountain Freight set, 83	NRS	NRS			
1353	Southern Streak set, 1983-85	NRS	NRS			
1354	Northern Freight Flyer set, 1983-85	NRS	NRS			
1355	Train Display Case set 1355, 83	—	40			
1355	Commando Assault Train set, 1983-84	100	160			
1359	Train Display Case set 1355, 83	—	40			
1361	Gold Coast Limited set, 1983	650	800			
1380	US Steel Industrial Switcher set, 1973-75	NRS	NRS			
1381	Cannonball set, 1973-84	NRS	NRS			
1381	Cannonball set, 1975	NRS	NRS			
1382	Yardmaster set, 1974	NRS	NRS			
1383	Santa Fe Freight set, 1973-75	NRS	NRS			
1384	Southern Express set, 1974-76	NRS	NRS			
1385	Blue Streak Freight set, 73-74	NRS	NRS			
1386	Rock Island Express set, 73-74	NRS	NRS			
1388	Golden State Arrow set, 74-75	NRS	NRS			
1390	Sears 7-unit set, 1973, uncat.	NRS	NRS			
1392	79C95224C Sears 8-unit set, 1973, uncatalogued	NRS	NRS			
1393	79C95223C Sears 6-unit set, 1973, uncatalogued	NRS	NRS			
1395	J. C. Penney set, 1973, uncat.	NRS	NRS			
1402	Chessie System set, 1984-85 catalogued, 1985 uncatalogued	NRS	NRS			
1403	R V Express set, 1984-85	190	225			

		Exc	LN	Color	Cond	$
1450	Service Station set, 1974, uncat.	400	450	___	___	___
1451	Erie Lackawanna Limited set, 84	550	625	___	___	___
1460	Grand National set, 1974	NRS	NRS	___	___	___
1461	Black Diamond set, 1975	NRS	NRS	___	___	___
1463	Coca-Cola Special set, 74, uncat.	175	220	___	___	___
1463	Coco-Cola Special set, 1975	175	225	___	___	___
1487	Broadway Limited set, 1974-75	325	375	___	___	___
1489	Santa Fe Double Diesel set, 74	NRS	NRS	___	___	___
1489	S F Double Diesel set, 1975-76	NRS	NRS	___	___	___
1492	79N96185C Sears 7-unit set, 1974, uncatalogued	NRS	NRS	___	___	___
1493	79N96185C Sears 7-unit set, 1974, uncatalogued	NRS	NRS	___	___	___
1499	J. C. Penney Great Express set, 1974, uncatalogued	NRS	NRS	___	___	___
1501	(See 18003)					
1501	Midland Freight set, 1985-86	NRS	NRS	___	___	___
1502	Yard Chief set, 1985-86	225	275	___	___	___
1506	Sears Centennial set, 85, uncat.	NRS	NRS	___	___	___
1512	See 1501 Midland Freight set					
1512	J. C. Penney Midland Freight set, 1986, uncatalogued	NRS	NRS	___	___	___
1549	Toys 'R Us Heavy Iron set, 1985, uncatalogued	NRS	NRS	___	___	___
1552	B N Limited set, 1985	—	575	___	___	___
1560	North American Express set, 75	300	375	___	___	___
1562	American Express Fast Freight Flyer set, 1985, uncatalogued	NRS	NRS	___	___	___
1577	Liberty Special set, 1975, uncat.	225	275	___	___	___
1579	Service Station set, 1975, uncat.	400	475	___	___	___
1581	Thunderball Freight set, 75-76	NRS	NRS	___	___	___
1582	Yard Chief set, 1975-76	NRS	NRS	___	___	___
1584	N & W Spirit of America set, 1975	275	325	___	___	___
1585	75th Anniversary Special set, 1975-77	220	250	___	___	___
1586	Chesapeake Flyer set, 1975-77	NRS	NRS	___	___	___
1587	Capitol Limited set, 1975	350	400	___	___	___
1594	Sears set, 1975, uncatalogued	NRS	NRS	___	___	___
1595	79C9716C Sears 6-unit Diesel set, 1975, uncatalogued	NRS	NRS	___	___	___
1602	Nickel Plate Special set, 1986	—	195	___	___	___
1602	Nickel Plate Special set, 1986, uncatalogued	NRS	NRS	___	___	___
1606	Sears Centennial set, 86, uncat.	NRS	NRS	___	___	___
1608	American Express General set, 1986, uncatalogued	NRS	NRS	___	___	___
1615	Cannonball Express set, 1986	85	95	___	___	___

		Exc	LN	Color	Cond	$
1632	Santa Fe Work Train Service Station set, 1986, uncatalogued	245	270			
1652	B & O Freight set, 1986	190	230			
1658	Town House set, 1986, uncat.	NRS	NRS			
1660	Yard Boss set, 1976	NRS	NRS			
1661	Rock Island Line set, 1976-77	95	125			
1662	The Black River Freight set, 1976-78	NRS	NRS			
1663	Amtrak Lake Shore Limited set, 1976-77	220	275			
1664	I C Freight set, 1976-77	350	400			
1665	N Y C Empire State Express set, 1976	550	600			
1672	Service Station set, 1976, uncat.	300	350			
1685	True Value Freight Flyer set, 1986, uncatalogued	NRS	NRS			
1686	Kaybee Freight Flyer set, 1986, uncatalogued	NRS	NRS			
1693	Toys 'R Us Rock Island Special set, 1976, uncatalogued	NRS	NRS			
1694	Toys 'R Us Black River Special set, 1976, uncatalogued	NRS	NRS			
1696	Sears set, 1976, uncatalogued	NRS	NRS			
1698	True Value set, 1976, uncat.	NRS	NRS			
1760	Steel Haulers set, 1977-78	NRS	NRS			
1761	Trains n' Truckin Cargo King set, 1977-78	NRS	NRS			
1762	The Wabash Cannonball set, 1977	NRS	NRS			
1764	The Heartland Express set, 1977	275	325			
1765	Rocky Mountain Special set, 1977	NRS	NRS			
1766	Service Station set, 1977, uncat.	400	450			
1776	B & A GP-9 pow. (w/cab.), 76	100	160			
1776	N & W N5C Caboose, 1976	30	35			
(1776)	N & W GP-9 powered, 1976	100	125			
1776	Seaboard U36B powered, 1976	100	125			
1790	Lionel Leisure Steel Hauler set, 1977, uncatalogued	NRS	NRS			
1791	Toys 'R Us Steel Hauler set, 1977, uncatalogued	NRS	NRS			
1792	True Value set, 1977, uncat.	NRS	NRS			
1793	Toys 'R Us Black River Freight, 1977, uncatalogued	NRS	NRS			
1796	J. C. Penney Cargo Master set, 1977, uncatalogued	NRS	NRS			
1860	Workin' On The Railroad Timberline set, 1978	NRS	NRS			

		Exc	LN	Color	Cond	$
862	Workin' On The Railroad Logging Empire set, 1978	75	90	___	___	___
864	S F Double Diesel set, 1978-79	NRS	NRS	___	___	___
865	Chesapeake Flyer set, 1978-79	NRS	NRS	___	___	___
866	Great Plains Express set, 1978	NRS	NRS	___	___	___
866	Great Plains Express set, 1979	NRS	NRS	___	___	___
867	Milwaukee Limited set, 1978	350	400	___	___	___
868	Service Station set, 1978, uncat.	225	275	___	___	___
892	J. C. Penney Logging Empire set, 1978, uncatalogued	NRS	NRS	___	___	___
893	Toys 'R Us Logging Empire set, 1978, uncatalogued	NRS	NRS	___	___	___
900	(See 18502)					
960	Midnight Flyer set, 1979-81	NRS	NRS	___	___	___
962	Wabash Cannonball set, 1979	NRS	NRS	___	___	___
963	Black River Freight set, 79-81	NRS	NRS	___	___	___
963	Black River Freight set, 1980	NRS	NRS	___	___	___
964	Radio Control Express set, 1979			Not Manufactured		
965	Smokey Mountain Line, 1979	NRS	NRS	___	___	___
1970	Southern Pacific Limited set, 79	550	650	___	___	___
1970	(See 8615)					
1971	Quaker City Limited set, 1979	400	460	___	___	___
1984	T T O S Sacramento Northern Boxcar, 1984	80	100	___	___	___
1985	T T O S Snowbird Quad Hopper, 1985	NRS	NRS	___	___	___
1987	(See 18605; steam)					
1987	(See 16310; gondola)					
1987	(See 16205; boxcar)					
1987	(See 16311; flatcar)					
1987	(See 16507; caboose)					
1989	(See 18614)					
1990	Mystery Glow Midnight Flyer set, 1979, uncatalogued	NRS	NRS	___	___	___
1991	J. C. Penney Wabash Cannonball Deluxe Express set, 1979, uncatalogued	NRS	NRS	___	___	___
1993	Toys 'R Us Midnight Flyer set, 1979, uncatalogued	NRS	NRS	___	___	___
2100	(See 18006)					
2110	Graduated Trestle, 1971-87	10	12	___	___	___
2111	Elevated Trestle, 1971-87	10	12	___	___	___
2113	Tunnel Portals (2), 1984-87	5	6	___	___	___
2115	Dwarf Signal, 1984-87	11	13	___	___	___
2117	Block Target Signal, 1985-87	17	21	___	___	___
2122	Extension Bridge, 1977-87	30	40	___	___	___
2125	Whistling Freight Station, 1971	60	75	___	___	___
2126	Whistling Freight Shed, 1976-87	25	35	___	___	___
2127	Diesel Horn Shed, 1976-87	25	35	___	___	___

		Exc	LN	Color	Cond	$
2128	Auto. Switchman, 1983-85	30	40			
2129	Illum. Freight Station, 1983-85	30	35			
2133	Illum. Freight Station, 1972-83	20	30			
2140	Automatic Banjo Signal, 1970-84	25	30			
2145	Automatic Gateman, 1970-84	25	30			
2146	Crossing Gate, 1970-71	15	20			
2151	Automatic Semaphore, 1978-83	25	30			
2152	Crossing Gate, 1972-86	25	35			
2154	Highway Flasher, 1970-87	20	25			
2156	Station Platform, 1971	35	50			
2162	Gate and Signal, 1970-87	20	25			
2163	Block Target Signal, 1970- 78	20	25			
2170	Street Lamps (3), 1970-87	20	25			
2171	Goose Neck Lamps (2), 1980-83	20	30			
2175	Sandy Andy Kit, 1976-79	30	50			
2180	Road Sign Set, 1977-87	3	5			
2181	Telephone Poles, 1977-87	3	5			
2195	Floodlight Tower, 1970-72	45	60			
2199	Microwave Tower, 1972-75	35	60			
2214	Girder Bridge, 1970-87	8	10			
2256	Station Platform, 1973-81	15	20			
2256	Station Platform T C A, 1975	25	35			
2260	Bumpers (Set of 3), 1970-73	25	40			
2260	Bumpers (Set of 3), 1986	—	3			
2280	Bumpers (Set of 3), 1973-80, 1983	3	5			
2281	Black Bumpers (Set of 3), 1983	15	18			
2282	Bumpers (Pair), 1983	25	35			
2283	Die-cast Bumpers, red (pr.), 84-85	10	15			
2290	Lighted Bump. (pr.), 1974-85	10	12			
2292	Station Platform, 1985-87	6	10			
2300	Oper. Oil Drum Loader, 1983	75	100			
2301	Operating Sawmill, 1981-83	65	85			
2302	U P Gantry Crane Kit, 1981-82	15	25			
2303	S F Gantry Crane Kit, 1980-81	20	30			
2305	Operating Oil Derrick, 1981-83	100	145			
2306	Operating Icing Station and "6700" Car, 1982-83	195	235			
2307	Billboard Light, 1983-84	15	25			
2308	Animated Newsstand, 1982-83	120	145			
2309	Mechanical Gate, 1982-87	2	4			
2310	Gate and Signal, 1973-75	3	5			
2311	Mechanical Semaphore, 1982-87	2	4			
2312	Mechanical Semaphore, 1973-75	5	6			
2313	Floodlight Tower, 1975-83	20	25			
2314	Searchlight Tower, 1975-83	20	30			
2315	Oper. Coaling Station, 1984-85	90	120			
2316	N & W Operating Gantry Crane, 1983-84	110	125			

		Exc	LN	Color	Cond	$
2317	Operating Drawbridge, 1975-81	60	75	___	___	___
2318	Operating Control Tower, 83-84	55	75	___	___	___
2319	Watchtower, illuminated, 75-80	20	30	___	___	___
2320	Flagpole Kit, 1983-87	10	15	___	___	___
2321	Operating Sawmill, 1984-85	60	100	___	___	___
2323	Oper. Freight Station, 1984-85	60	75	___	___	___
2324	Oper. Switch Tower, 1984-85	55	65	___	___	___
2383	Illum. Bumpers, die-cast, 1987	—	12	___	___	___
2390	Lionel Mirror, 1982	50	65	___	___	___
2494	Rotary Beacon, 1972-74	40	50	___	___	___
2709	Rico Station Kit, 1981-85	20	30	___	___	___
2710	Billboards (5), 1970-84	5	6	___	___	___
2714	Tunnel, 1975-77	40	50	___	___	___
2716	Short Extension Bridge, 1988	10	15	___	___	___
2717	Short Extension Bridge, 1977-83	3	5	___	___	___
2718	Barrel Platform Kit, 1977-83	2	4	___	___	___
2719	Signal Tower Kit, 1977-83,	2	4	___	___	___
2719	Watchman's Shanty Kit, 1977-83	2	4	___	___	___
2720	Lumber Shed Kit, 1977-83	2	4	___	___	___
2721	Operating Log Mill, 1979	3	5	___	___	___
2722	Barrel Loader, 1979	3	5	___	___	___
2723	Barrel Loader, 1984	3	5	___	___	___
2729	Water Tower Building Kit, 1985			Not Manufactured		
2783	Manual Freight Station Kit, 81-85	7	10	___	___	___
2784	Freight Platform Kit, 1981-87	6	9	___	___	___
2785	Engine House Kit, 1974-77	30	40	___	___	___
2786	Freight Platform Kit, 1974-77	4	7	___	___	___
2787	Freight Station Kit, 1974-77, 1983	7	10	___	___	___
2788	Coaling Station Kit, 1975-77	20	40	___	___	___
2789	Water Tower Kit, 1975-80	7	10	___	___	___
2790	Building Kit Assortment, 1983	NRS	NRS	___	___	___
2791	Cross Country Set, 1970-71	25	35	___	___	___
2792	Layout Starter Pak, 1980-83	10	25	___	___	___
2792	Whistle Stop Set, 1970-71	25	35	___	___	___
2793	Alamo Junction Set, 1970-71	25	35	___	___	___
2796	Grain Elevator Kit, 1977	60	75	___	___	___
2797	Rico Station Kit, 1976	30	45	___	___	___
2900	Lockon, 1970-85	1	1.25	___	___	___
2901	Track Clips (12), 1970-85	2	5	___	___	___
2905	Lockon and Wire, 1972-85	.85	1.50	___	___	___
2909	Smoke Fluid, 1977-85	1.50	3	___	___	___
2910-1	Contactor, circa 1984-91	—	CP	___	___	___
2911	Smoke Pellets, 1970-72	10	15	___	___	___
2927	Maint. Kit, 1970-71, 1977-87	5	7	___	___	___
2951	Track Book, 1976-80, 1983	.75	2	___	___	___
2952	Track Accessories Manual, 1985	.75	1	___	___	___
2953	Track and Accessory Manual, 1977-85	1.25	2	___	___	___

		Exc	LN	Color	Cond	$
2960	Lionel 75th Anniv. Book, 1975	8	10			
2980	Magnetic Conv. Coupler, 71, 79	1	2			
2985	The Lionel Train Book, 1986	7	10			
3000	(See 18009)					
3080	Train Display Layout	175	250			
3100	G N Steam 4-8-4, 1981	495	575			
3300	(See 33000)					
3764	L O T S, Kahn Boxcar, 1981	—	50			
4000	(See 18812)					
4044	Transformer 45-W, 1970-71	3	5			
4045	Safety Transformer, 1970-71	3	4			
4050	Safety Transformer, 1972-79	3	4			
4060	Power Master, Trans. 1980-91	—	CP			
4065	Commando Set, DC Transformer, for set 1355, 1986	15	25			
4065	DC Hobby Transformer, 1981-83	3	4			
4090	Power Master, Trans., 70-81, 83	40	55			
4125	Transformer 25-W, 1972	3	4			
4150	Trainmaster Transformer, 76-78	6	12			
4250	Trainmaster Transformer	6	12			
4410	(See 18007)					
4449	(See 8307)					
4501	(See 8309)					
4651	Trainmaster Transformer, 1978-79	2	3			
4690	Transformer, Type MW, Solid-state, 1986-87	—	85			
4851	Transformer, 1987-88	3	4			
4870	DC Hobby Transformer and Throttle Controller, 1977-78	3	4			
4935	(See 8150)					
5001	Curved Track (O27), 1985	NRS	NRS			
5012	Curved Track, 4 pcs. (O27), 1970-91	—	CP			
5013	Curved Track (O27)	.50	.55			
5014	Half-Curved (O27), 1980-83	.50	.75			
5016	3-foot Straight Track (O27), 87	—	2.25			
5017	Straight Track, 4 pcs. (O27), 80-83	—	3.50			
5018	Straight Track (O27)	.50	.75			
5019	Half-Straight Track (O27), 86-88	.50	.75			
5020	90° Crossover (O27), 1970-88	3.50	4.75			
5021	Manual Left Switch (O27), 86-88	8	13			
5022	Manual Right Switch (O27), 86-88	8	13			
5023	45° Crossover (O27), 1970-88	4	6.50			
5024	Straight Track (O27)	—	2.25			
5025	Manumatic Uncoupler, 1971-75	1	2			
5027	Manual Switches, pair (O27)	15	26			
5030	Track Expander Set, 1972	—	25			
5030	Layout Set, 1978-80, 1983	17	25			

		Exc	LN	Color	Cond	$
31	Train Access Kit/Ford Marketing Corporation, 1972	NRS	NRS	___	___	___
33	Curved Track (O27), 1986-88	.30	.75	___	___	___
38	Straight Track (O27), 1986-88	.30	.75	___	___	___
41	Insulator Pins (dz.) (O27), 86-88	.50	1	___	___	___
42	Steel Pins (8/pack) (O27), 86-88	.40	.75	___	___	___
44	Curved Trk. Ballast (O42), 87-88	—	2.25	___	___	___
45	Wide Radius Track Ballast (O27), 1987	—	2.25	___	___	___
46	Curved Trk. Ballast (O27), 1987	—	2.25	___	___	___
47	Straight Trk. Ballast (O27), 1987	—	2.25	___	___	___
49	Curved Track (O42)	—	1.10	___	___	___
90	Manual Switches (3 pr.), 1983	60	80	___	___	___
100	(See 18001)					
113	Wide Radius Curved Track (O27), 1986-87	1.10	1.50	___	___	___
121	Left R.C. Switch (O27), 1986-88	14	20	___	___	___
122	Right R.C. Switch (O27), 86-88	14	20	___	___	___
125	R.C. Switches, pair (O27), 1986	28	40	___	___	___
132	R.C. Right Switch (O27), 86-88	33	40	___	___	___
133	R.C. Left Switch (O), 1986-88	33	40	___	___	___
149	R.C. Uncoupling Trk. (O), 86-88	3.50	7.25	___	___	___
165	R.C. Switches (O72), right, 1987	—	50	___	___	___
166	R.C. Switches (O72), left, 1987	—	50	___	___	___
167	Remote Switch (O42), right, 1988	—	25	___	___	___
168	Remote Switch (O42), left, 1988	—	25	___	___	___
193	R.C. Switches (3 pr.) (O27), 83	90	110	___	___	___
340	(See 18005)					
500	Straight Track (O), 1971	.75	1.25	___	___	___
501	Curved Track (O), 1971	.75	1.25	___	___	___
502	Remote Control Track, 10", 1971	5	8	___	___	___
504	Half-Curved (O), 1983, 1985-88	—	1.05	___	___	___
505	Half-Straight (O), 1983, 1985-88	—	1.05	___	___	___
510	Curved Track (O)	.75	1.25	___	___	___
520	90° Crossover (O), 1971	5	7	___	___	___
522	3-foot Straight Track, 1987	—	3.75	___	___	___
523	Straight Track, 40-inch	—	5	___	___	___
530	Remote Uncoupling Section (O), 1986-88	11	13	___	___	___
540	90° Crossover (O), 1981-88	7	8	___	___	___
543	Insulator Pins (12) (O), 1970	.75	1	___	___	___
545	45° Crossover (O), 1982	—	13	___	___	___
551	Steel Pins (12/pack) (O), 1970	.75	1	___	___	___
560	Curved Track, (O72) Ballast, 87	—	2.25	___	___	___
561	Curved Track, (O) Ballast, 1987	—	2.25	___	___	___
562	Straight Track, (O) Ballast, 1987	—	2.25	___	___	___
572	Wide Radius Curved Track (O72), 1986-88	1.25	2	___	___	___

		Exc	LN	Color	Cond	$
5600	Curved Track, 1973	—	1.75			
5601	Card of Four Curved Track, 1973	—	7			
5602	Card of Four Roadbed Ballast, Curved Track, 1973-74	4	7			
5605	Straight Track, 1973	1	2			
5606	Card of Four Straight Track, 1973	4	8			
5607	Card of Four Roadbed Ballast, Straight Track, 1973	4	8			
5620	Left Manual Switch, 1973-74	—	25			
5625	Left Remote Switch, 1973	NRS	NRS			
5630	Right Manual Switch, 1973-74	—	25			
5635	Right Remote Switch, 1973	NRS	NRS			
5640	Left Switch Roadbed Pcs. (2), 73	—	10			
5650	Right Switch Roadbed Pcs. (2), 73	—	8			
5655	Lockon, 1973	—	1.50			
5660	Terminal Track w/Lockon, 1973	—	3.50			
5700	Oppenheimer Wood. Reefer, 81	25	45			
5701	Dairymen's League Reefer, 1981	20	25			
5702	Nat. Dairy Despatch Reefer, 81	20	25			
5703	North American Despatch Reefer, 1981	20	25			
5704	Budweiser Woodside Reefer, 81	45	55			
5705	Ball Glass Jars Wood. Reefer, 81	25	30			
5706	Lindsay Bros. Wood. Reefer, 81	25	30			
5707	American Refrig. Reefer, 1981	20	25			
5708	Armour Woodside Reefer, 82-83	17	20			
5709	R E A Woodside Reefer, 82-83	30	45			
5710	C P Wood. Reefer, 1982-83	17	20			
5710	L C A C Canadian Pacific Reefer, Woodside, 1983	NRS	NRS			
5711	Commercial Express Woodside Reefer, 1982-83	17	20			
5712	Lionel Woodside Reefer, 1982	200	300			
5713	Cotton Belt Wood. Reefer, 1983	15	20			
5714	Michigan Central Reefer, 1983	15	20			
5714	L C C A M C Reefer, 1985	—	NRS			
5715	Santa Fe Reefer, orange, 1983	20	25			
5716	Vermont Central Reefer, 1983	15	20			
5717	A T & S F Bunk Car, gray, 1984	40	55			
5718	(See 9849)					
5719	Canadian National Reefer, 1984	15	20			
5720	Great Northern Reefer, 1985	85	125			
5721	SOO Line Woodside Reefer, 85	15	20			
5722	Nickel Plate Woodside Reefer, 85	15	20			
5724	Pennsylvania Bunk Car, 1985	20	25			
5726	Southern Bunk Car, 1985	30	40			
5727	U. S. Marines Bunk Car, 1985	15	20			
5728	Canadian Pacific Bunk Car, 1986	15	20			

		Exc	LN	Color	Cond	$
5730	Strasburg R R Reefer, 1985-86	15	20			
5731	L & N Woodside Reefer, 85-86	12	15			
5732	Central R R of N J Reefer, 85-86	20	30			
5733	Lionel Lines Bunk Car, 1986	40	50			
5734-85	R E A T C A Reefer, 1985	—	150			
5735	N Y C Bunk Car, gray, 1985-86	35	45			
5739	B & O Tool Car, Gray, 1986	40	50			
5745	A T & S F Bunk Car, 1986	40	50			
5760	A T & S F Tool Car, 1986	40	50			
5800	Bumper Sticker, 1987	—	1.50			
5801	Lighter, 1987-90	—	3.50			
5802	Lapel Pin, 1987-91	—	CP			
5803	License Plate, 1987, 1991	—	CP			
5804	Epoxy Key Chain, 1987	—	4.50			
5805	Ash Tray, 1987-90,	—	6.50			
5806	Coffee Mug, 1987-90	—	7.50			
5807	Sport Cap, 1987	—	8			
5808	Brass Key Chain, 1987-90	—	8			
5809	Engineer's Gloves, 1987	—	8.50			
5810	Sleeping Boy Poster, 1987	—	9			
5811	Nickel Plate Special Poster, 1987	—	9			
5812	Rail Blazer Poster, 1987	—	9			
5813	Lionel T-Shirt, 1987	—	11			
5817	Portable Tool Kit, 1987	—	11.50			
5818	Mini-Mag-Lite Flashlight, 1987	—	20			
5819	Pen and Pencil Set, 1987-90	—	20			
5820	Travel Alarm Clock, 1987	—	20			
5821	Beverage Coaster Set, 1987	—	70			
5822	Wrist Watch, 1987	—	110			
5823	45° O Gauge Crossover	4	6			
5823	Bumper Sticker, 1989-90	—	1.50			
5824	Note Pads, 1989-90	—	2.50			
5825	Fabric Patch, 1989-91	—	CP			
5826	Pennant, 1989-91	—	CP			
5827	A. F. Pennant, 1989-91	—	CP			
5828	License Plate, 1989-91	—	CP			
5829	Circle L Lapel Pin, 1989-91	—	CP			
5830	A. F. Lapel Pin, 1989-91	—	CP			
5831	Polyurethane Beverage Can Holders, 1989-90	—	5.50			
5832	Carpenter's Apron, 1989-90	—	7			
5833	Carpenter's Apron, 1989	—	7			
5834	Beverage Mug, 1989-91	—	CP			
5835	Engineer's Cap, 1989-91	—	CP			
5836-42	Lionel T-shirts, 1989-90	—	11			
5843	Poster Set (5810-11-12), 1989-90	—	15			
5844-46	Sweatshirts (Children's), 89-90	—	16			
5847	Tote Bag (Lionel), 1989-91	—	CP			

		Exc	LN	Color	Cond	$
5848	Tote Bag (Flyer), 1989-91	—	CP			
5849-52	Sweatshirts (Adults'), 1989-90	—	16			
5853	Men's Tie, 1989-90	—	22			
5854	Women's Tie, 1989-90	—	22			
5855	Swiss Army Knife, 1989-91	—	CP			
5856	Pocket Watch, 1989-90	—	26			
5857	Welcome Mat, 1989-90	—	30			
5858	Director's Chair, 1989-91	—	CP			
5859	Pennant, 1991	—	CP			
5860	All Aboard Cookbook, 1991	—	CP			
5861-67	Lionel T-shirts, 1991	—	CP			
5868	Bumper Sticker, 1991	—	CP			
5869	Loco. Christmas Ornament, 1991	—	CP			
5870	Caboose Christmas Ornament, 91	—	CP			
5871	Station Christmas Ornament, 1991	—	CP			
5872	Engr. Christmas Ornament, 1991	—	CP			
5873	Santa Christmas Ornament, 1991	—	CP			
5874	Crossing Signal Christmas Ornament, 1991	—	CP			
5875	Lionel Stuffed Lion Doll, 1991	—	CP			
5876	Men's Tie, 1991	—	CP			
5877	Women's Tie, 1991	—	CP			
5878	Sport Cap, 1991	—	CP			
5900	AC/DC Converter, 1979-81, 1983	4	6			
5906	Sound Activation Button, 89-91	—	CP			
6076	T T O S Santa Fe Hopper, 70	NRS	NRS			
6076	L V Short Hopper, 1970	20	25			
6100	Ontario Northland Quad, 1981-82	30	40			
6100	L C C A O N Hopper, 1982	NRS	NRS			
6101	B N Quad Hop., green, 1981, 83	15	25			
6102	G N Quad (FARR #3), 1981	35	50			
6103	C N Quad Hopper, 1981	25	35			
6104	Southern Quad Hopper with coal (FARR #4), 1984-85	75	85			
6105	Reading Oper. Short Hopper, 82	55	65			
6106	N & W Quad Hopper, gray, 1982	35	45			
6107	Shell Quad Hopper, yellow, 1982	15	20			
6109	C & O Oper. Short Hopper, 1983	25	40			
6110	MoPac Quad Hopper, black, 1983	15	25			
6111	L O T S L & N Quad, 1983	—	50			
6111	L & N Quad Hopper, gray, 1983	15	25			
6112	L C C A Commonwealth Edison Hopper, 1983	75	95			
6113	Illinois Central Short Hopper, 85	10	15			
6114	C & N W Quad Hopper, 1983	105	125			
6115	Southern Quad with Coal, 1983	10	20			
6116	SOO Line Ore Car, 1985	35	45			
6117	Erie Operating Short Hop., 1985	25	35			

		Exc	LN	Color	Cond	$
6118	Erie-Lackawanna Quad, 1985	45	50			
6122	Penn Central Ore Car, 1985	35	45			
6123	P R R Quad (FARR #5), gray, 85	45	55			
6124	D & H Quad Hopper, red, 1984	15	25			
6126	Canadian National Ore Car, 1986	25	30			
6127	(See 5735)					
6127	Northern Pacific Ore Car, 1986	30	35			
6131	I C Terminal Quad Hop., 85-86	17	25			
6134	B N A C F Short Hopper, 1986	150	200			
6135	C & N W A C F Hopper, 1986	150	200			
6137	N K P Road Hopper, 1986	10	15			
6138	B & O Quad Hopper, 1986	20	30			
6150	Santa Fe Hopper, blue, 1985-86	10	15			
6177	Reading Short Hopper, brown, 86	20	25			
6200	F E C Gondola, red, 1981	15	30			
6200	(See 18010; 1991)					
6200	(See 8404; 1984-85)					
6201	Union Pacific Gondola, 1982-83	25	35			
6202	Western MD Gondola w/coal, 82	35	45			
6203	Black Cave Gondola, 1982	6	8			
6205	Canadian Pacific Gondola, 1983	25	30			
6206	C & I M Gondola, red, 1985	10	15			
6207	Southern Gon., black (O27), 1984	6	8			
6208	B & O "Chessie" Gon., 1983-84	25	30			
6209	N Y C Gon. w/coal (Std. O), 85	50	75			
6210	Erie-Lackawanna Gondola, 1985	20	30			
6211	C & O Gondola (O27), 1984	—	10			
6211	L O T S C & O Gondola, 1986	—	35			
6214	Lionel Lines Gondola, 1985	25	40			
6230	Erie Reefer (Std. O), 1986	135	155			
6231	Railgon Gondola (Std. O), 1986	140	200			
6232	I C Boxcar (Std. O), 1986	135	155			
6233	C P Flat. w/stakes (Std. O), 86	135	155			
6234	B N Boxcar, green (Std. O), 85	30	40			
6235	B N Boxcar, green (Std. O), 85	30	40			
6236	B N Boxcar, green (Std. O), 85	30	40			
6237	B N Boxcar, green (Std. O), 85	30	40			
6238	B N Boxcar, green (Std. O), 85	30	40			
6239	B N Boxcar (Std. O), 1986	30	40			
6251	N Y C Oper. Coal Dump, 85-86	15	20			
6254	N K P Road Gondola, 1986	10	12			
6258	A T S F Gondola, 1985-86	—	6			
X6260	N Y C Gondola, 1985	15	18			
6272	A T & S F Long Gondola, 1986	20	25			
6300	Corn Products 3-D Tank Car, 81	25	35			
6301	Gulf 1-D Tank Car, 1981-82	20	25			
6302	Quaker State 3-D Tank, 81-82	30	40			
6304	G N 1-D Tank (FARR #3), 1981	50	65			

		Exc	LN	Color	Cond	$
6305	B C 1-D Tank Car, 1981	50	65			
6306	Southern 1-D Tank Car (FARR #4) 1984-85	45	60			
6307	Pennsylvania Railroad 1-D Tank Car (FARR #5), 1985	50	65			
6308	Alaska 1-D Short Tank Car, 1982	25	30			
6310	Shell 2-D Tank Car (O27), 1983	15	20			
6312	C & O 2-D Tank Car (O27), 84	20	30			
6313	Lionel Lines 1-D Tank Car, 1985	40	55			
6314	B & O 3-D Tank Car, black, 86	35	50			
6315	T C A Pittsburgh Tank, 1972	75	95			
6317	Gulf 2-D Tank Car (O27), 1984	15	20			
6323	L C C A Virginia Chemical 1-D Tank, 86	35	45			
6325	(See 6579)					
6357	Frisco 1-D Tank Car, black, 1983	50	65			
6401	Virginian B/W Caboose, 1981	35	40			
6403	Amtrak Vista Dome, 1976-77	45	65			
6404	Amtrak Pullman, 1976-77	45	65			
6405	Amtrak Pullman, 1976-77	45	65			
6406	Amtrak Observation, 1976-77	45	65			
6410	Amtrak Pullman, 1977-78	30	50			
6411	Amtrak Pullman, 1977-78	30	50			
6412	Amtrak Vista Dome, 1977-78	30	50			
6420	Reading Maint. Caboose, 81-82	15	20			
6421	Cowen B/W Caboose, 1982	35	40			
6422	Duluth Missabe B/W Cab., 81-82	20	25			
6425	Erie-Lack. B/W Caboose, 1984	35	40			
6426	Reading Maint. Caboose, 82-83	10	12			
6427	B N Maintenance Caboose, 1983	10	15			
6428	C & N W Maintenance Cab., 85	12	15			
6430	Santa Fe SP Caboose, 1983	6	8			
6431	Southern Bay Window Caboose (FARR #4), 1983-84	35	45			
6432	Union Pacific SP Caboose, 1981	10	12			
6433	C P B/W Caboose, 1981-82	40	60			
6434	S S R R, 1983	6	8			
6435	U.S. Transfer Caboose, 1983-84	—	20			
6438	G N B/W Cab. (FARR #3), 81	35	50			
6439	Reading B/W Caboose, 1985-86	20	30			
6441	Alaska B/W Caboose, 1982-83	25	30			
6446-25	N & W Quad Hopper, 1970	150	175			
6449	Wendy's N5C Caboose, 1981-82	40	50			
6464-500	Timken Boxcar, 1970	100	150			
6464-1970	T C A Special Boxcar, 70	125	160			
6464-1971	T C A Special Boxcar, 71	200	250			
6476-135	LV Hopper, 1970-71	NRS	NRS			
6478	Black Cave SP Caboose, 1982	5	10			

		Exc	LN	Color	Cond	$
481	Rio Grande SP Caboose, 1983	6	8	___	___	___
482	Nibco Express SP Caboose, 1982	—	80	___	___	___
485	Chessie Caboose, 1984-85	—	10	___	___	___
491	Erie-Lack. Transfer Cab., 85-86	—	12	___	___	___
493	L & C B/W Caboose, 1986-87	20	25	___	___	___
494	A T & S F 4-Wheel Bobber Caboose, 1986	8	10	___	___	___
496	A T & S F Work Caboose, 1986	—	30	___	___	___
6500)	Lionel Transfer Car, 1980 (see 9233)					
504	L A S E R Helicopter, 1981-82	12	30	___	___	___
505	L A S E R Guidance, 1981-82	12	30	___	___	___
506	L A S E R Security Car, 1981-82	15	30	___	___	___
507	L A S E R Missile Car, 1981-82	12	30	___	___	___
508	C P Crane, 12-whl., 1981	45	70	___	___	___
509	Lionel 16-whl. Flat. w/girders, 81	60	75	___	___	___
510	Union Pacific Crane, 1982	50	75	___	___	___
515	U P Flatcar, 1986	—	10	___	___	___
521	N Y C Flat. w/stakes (Std. O), 85	55	70	___	___	___
522	C & N W Searchlight Car, 84-85	25	30	___	___	___
524	Erie-Lack. Crane, 12-whl., 1985	45	70	___	___	___
526	U. S. Marines Searchlight Car, 85	15	20	___	___	___
529	N Y C Searchlight Car, gray, 1985-86	20	25	___	___	___
531	Express Mail Flat. w/vans, 85-86	15	25	___	___	___
560	Bucyrus Erie Crane Car, 8-wheel, 1971	125	150	___	___	___
561	Flatcar w/Cruise Missile, 83-84	—	25	___	___	___
562	Flatcar with Barrels, 1983-84	—	25	___	___	___
564	Flat. w/2 U S M C Tanks, 83-84	—	25	___	___	___
567	L C C A I C Gulf Crane, 1985	60	75	___	___	___
573	Redwood Valley Express Flatcar with log dump, 1984-85	—	15	___	___	___
574	Redwood Valley Express Short Crane, 1984	—	15	___	___	___
575	Redwood Valley Express Flatcar, 1984-85	—	15	___	___	___
576	A T S F Short Crane, 1985-86	—	12	___	___	___
579	N Y C Crane, black, 8-wheel, 1985-86	30	50	___	___	___
582	T T O S Portland Flatcar, with lumber load, 1986	—	100	___	___	___
585	Penn Flatcar w/fences, yel., 1986	—	10	___	___	___
587	W & A General, 1986	20	30	___	___	___
593	A T & S F Crane, 1986	—	35	___	___	___
670	(See 9378)					
700	Pacific Fruit Express Operating Ice Car, 1982 (see 2306)					
900	N & W Ext. Vis. Caboose, 1982	90	120	___	___	___
901	Ont. Northland Ext. Vis. Cab., 82	50	75	___	___	___

		Exc	LN	Color	Cond	$
6903	S F Extended Vision Cab., 1983	100	125			
6904	U P Extended Vision Cab., 1983	100	150			
6905	Nickel Plate Ext. Vis. Cab., 1984	75	100			
6906	Erie-Lack. Ext. Vis. Cab., 1985	75	100			
6907	N Y C Woodside Caboose, 86	150	200			
6908	Pennsylvania N5C Caboose, 85	65	95			
6910	N Y C Extended Vision Cab., 85	85	115			
6912	Redwood Valley Express Caboose, 1983-84	—	20			
6913	B N Extended Vision Cab., 1986	85	115			
6916	N Y C Work Cab., gray, 1985-86	12	15			
6917	J C Ext. Vis. Caboose, 1986	40	50			
6918	B & O SP Type Caboose, 1986	—	15			
6919	Nickel Plate Caboose, 1986	—	10			
6920	B & A Woodside Caboose, 86	125	175			
6921	P R R SP Type Caboose, 1986	—	10			
6926	T C A New Orleans Ext. Vis. Caboose, 1986	—	60			
7100	Huff 'n Puff Booklet, 1975	—	.25			
7200	Streamline Quicksilver Coach, 1982-83	35	50			
7201	Streamline Quicksilver Coach, 1982-83	35	50			
7202	Quicksilver Observation, 1982-83	35	50			
(7203)	N & W "491" Diner, 1984	275	400			
7204	S P Daylight Diner, 1984	275	400			
7205	T C A Denver Combine, 1982	—	75			
7206	T C A Louisville Pullman, 1983	—	75			
7207	New York Central Diner, 1984	175	300			
7208	Pennsylvania Diner, 1984	175	250			
7210	Union Pacific Diner, 1985	125	225			
7211	S P Daylight Vista Dome, 1984	300	400			
7212	T C A Pittsburgh Pullman, 1984	—	75			
7215	B & O Old Time Coach, 1983	30	50			
7216	B & O Old Time Coach, 1983	30	50			
7217	B & O Old Time Baggage, 1983	30	50			
7220	I C Baggage, 1986	75	100			
7221	I C Combine, 1986	75	100			
7222	I C Coach, 1986	75	120			
7223	I C Coach, 1986	75	120			
7224	I C Diner, 1986	75	120			
7225	I C 12-Wheel Obs., 1986	75	120			
7227	Wab. 12-Whl. Diner, 1986-87	75	100			
7228	Wab. 12-Whl. Bagg. Car, 86-87	75	100			
7229	Wab. 12-Whl. Comb. Car, 86-87	75	100			
7230	Wabash 12-Whl. Coach, 86-87	75	100			
7231	Wabash 12-Whl. Coach, 86-87	75	100			
7232	Wabash 12-Whl. Obs. Car, 86-87	75	100			

		Exc	LN	Color	Cond	$
241	W & A Coach, 1986	30	50	___	___	___
242	W & A Baggage Car, 1986	30	50	___	___	___
301	N & W Stock Car, brown, 1982	40	50	___	___	___
302	T & P Stock Car (O27), 1983-84	10	15	___	___	___
303	Erie-Lack. Stock Car, blue, 1985	45	50	___	___	___
304	Southern "9459" Stock Car, 1983	60	75	___	___	___
309	Southern Short Stock Car, 85-86	10	15	___	___	___
312	W & A Stock Car, 1986	20	25	___	___	___
401	Chessie Stock Car (O27), red, 84	10	15	___	___	___
403	L C C A L N A C Boxcar, 1984	35	45	___	___	___
404	Jersey Central Boxcar, 1986	40	50	___	___	___
500	Lionel 75th Anniversary U36B					
	powered, 1975	80	100	___	___	___
501	Lionel 75th Anniv. Boxcar, 1975	15	20	___	___	___
502	Lionel 75th Anniv. Reefer, 1975	15	20	___	___	___
503	Lionel 75th Anniv. Reefer, 1975	15	20	___	___	___
504	Lionel 75th Anniv. Quad, 1975	20	25	___	___	___
505	Lionel 75th Anniv. Boxcar, 1975	15	20	___	___	___
506	Lionel 75th Anniv. Boxcar, 1975	15	20	___	___	___
507	Lionel 75th Anniv. Reefer, 1975	15	20	___	___	___
508	Lionel 75th Anniv. Cab., N5C, 75	20	30	___	___	___
509	Kentucky Fried Chicken, 1981-82	15	20	___	___	___
510	Red Lobster Reefer, 1981-82	20	30	___	___	___
511	Pizza Hut Reefer, 1981-82	20	25	___	___	___
512	Arthur Treacher's Reefer, 1982	20	25	___	___	___
513	Bonanza Reefer, 1982	20	25	___	___	___
514	Taco Bell Reefer, 1982	20	25	___	___	___
515	Denver Mint Car, 1982	75	85	___	___	___
517	Philadelphia Mint Car, 1982	45	55	___	___	___
518	Carson City Mint Car, 1983	35	50	___	___	___
519	Toy Fair Reefer, 1982	35	55	___	___	___
520	Nibco Boxcar, 1982	—	545	___	___	___
521	Toy Fair Reefer, 1983	35	50	___	___	___
522	New Orleans Mint Car, 1985	35	45	___	___	___
523	Toy Fair Refrigerator, 1984	150	175	___	___	___
524	Toy Fair Reefer, 1985	175	200	___	___	___
525	Toy Fair Boxcar, 86 (see 7925)	150	175	___	___	___
530	Dahlonega Mint Car, 1986	65	75	___	___	___
600	Frisco N5C "Spirit" Cab., 74-76	30	40	___	___	___
601	Delaware Boxcar, 1975-76	15	20	___	___	___
602	Pennsylvania Boxcar, 1975-76	20	30	___	___	___
603	New Jersey Boxcar, 1975-76	20	30	___	___	___
604	Georgia Boxcar, 1975-76	20	30	___	___	___
605	Connecticut Boxcar, 1975-76	20	30	___	___	___
606	Massachusetts Boxcar, 1975-76	20	30	___	___	___
607	Maryland Boxcar, 1975-76	20	30	___	___	___
608	South Carolina Boxcar, 1975-76	25	35	___	___	___
609	New Hampshire Boxcar, 75-76	35	45	___	___	___

		Exc	LN	Color	Cond	$
7610	Virginia Boxcar, 1976	150	195			
7611	New York Boxcar, 1976	60	75			
7612	North Carolina Boxcar, 1976	20	45			
7613	Rhode Island Boxcar, 1976	50	65			
7700	Uncle Sam Boxcar, 1976	60	75			
7701	Camel Boxcar, 1976-77	12	20			
7702	Prince Albert Boxcar, 1976-77	12	20			
7703	Beechnut Boxcar, 1976-77	12	20			
7704	Welcome Toy Fair Box., 76-77	175	200			
7705	Madison Toy Fair Boxcar, 1976	300	400			
7706	Sir Walter Raleigh Boxcar, 77-78	15	20			
7707	White Owl Boxcar, 1977-78	15	20			
7708	Winston Boxcar, 1977-78	15	20			
7709	Salem Boxcar, 1978	15	20			
7710	Mail Pouch Boxcar, 1978	25	30			
7711	El Producto Boxcar, 1978	25	30			
7712	A T & S F Box. (FARR #1), 79	35	45			
7714	Northern Pacific Boxcar, 1980	12	15			
7784	T C A Museum, 1984	30	35			
7800	Pepsi Boxcar, 1977	25	45			
7801	A & W Boxcar, 1977	15	30			
7802	Canada Dry Boxcar, 1977	20	30			
7803	Trains 'n Truckin' Boxcar, 1978	20	35			
7806	Season's Greetings Boxcar, 1976	80	100			
7807	Toy Fair Boxcar, 1977	150	175			
7808	N P Stock Car, 1977	50	65			
7809	Vernors Boxcar, 1978	15	25			
7810	Orange Crush Boxcar, 1978	15	25			
7811	Dr. Pepper Boxcar, 1978	15	25			
7812	T C A Houston Stock Car, 1977	35	45			
7813	Season's Greetings Boxcar, 77	150	175			
7814	Season's Greetings Boxcar, 78	175	200			
7815	Toy Fair Boxcar, 1978	125	150			
7816	Toy Fair Boxcar, 1979	125	150			
7817	Toy Fair Boxcar, 1980	125	150			
7900	Outlaw Car, 1982-83	11	14			
7901	Cop & Hobo Car, 1982-83	20	25			
7902	A T & S F Boxcar (O27), 82-83	6	8			
7903	Rock Boxcar (O27), 1983	6	8			
7904	San Diego Zoo Car (O27), 1983	30	35			
7905	Black Cave Boxcar, 1982	7	10			
7908	Tappan Boxcar (O27), 1982	50	70			
7909	L & N Boxcar (O27), 1983	10	15			
7910	Chessie Boxcar (O27), 1984	10	15			
7912	Geoffrey Car, 1982-83	100	125			
7913	Turtleback Zoo Giraffe Car, 1986	35	40			
7914	Geoffrey Car, 1985	100	135			
7920	Sears Centennial Boxcar, 85-86	—	55			

		Exc	LN	Color	Cond	$
7925	Erie Lackawanna Box. (O27), 86	8	12			
7926	N K P Boxcar (O27), 1986	8	11			
7930	True Value Box. (O27)	—	60			
7931	Town House TV & Appliances Boxcar, (O27), 1986	—	50			
7932	Kay Bee Toys Boxcar (O27), 86	—	50			
8001	Nickel Plate Steam 2-6-4, 1980	50	60			
8002	Union Pacific Steam 2-8-4, 1980	450	575			
8003	Chessie Steam 2-8-4, 1980	500	600			
8004	Rock Island Steam 4-4-0, 1980, 1982	150	170			
8004	(See 18004)					
8005	A T & S F Steam 4-4-0, 1980, 82	30	40			
8006	A C L Steam 4-6-4 (J. C. Penney's Special), 1980	700	1000			
8007	N Y N H & H Steam 2-6-4, 1980	40	50			
8008	Chessie Steam 4-4-2, 1980	50	75			
8010	A T & S F NW-2 Switcher, 1970	60	75			
8014	(See 18014)					
8020	(A) S F Alco powered, 1970-76	75	100			
8020	(B) S F Alco A dummy, 70-71	50	70			
8021	S F Alco B dummy, 71-72, 74-76	60	75			
8022	Santa Fe Alco A powered, 1971	125	185			
8023	Canadian National Alco A, 1970	60	75			
8025	C N Alco AA, 1971	150	225			
8030	I C GP-9 powered, 1970-71	85	125			
8031	C N GP-7 powered, 1970-71	70	125			
8040	Nickel Plate Steam 2-4-2, 70-72	20	30			
8040	Canadian Natl. Steam 2-4-2, 1971	50	100			
8041	N Y C Steam 2-4-2, 1970-71	30	40			
8041	P R R Steam 2-4-2, 1971	60	75			
8042	Grand Trunk Steam 2-4-2, 70, 72	30	40			
8043	Nickel Plate Steam 2-4-2, 1970	50	75			
8050	D & H U36C powered, 1980	125	175			
8051	D & H U36C dummy, 1980	100	125			
8054/8055	C & S Burlington F-3 AA, 1980	350	450			
8056	C & N W Trainmaster, 1980-81	300	395			
8057	Burlington NW-2 powered Switcher, 1980	75	150			
8059	Penn F-3 B dummy, green, 1980	300	400			
8060	Penn F-3 B dummy, tuscan, 80	300	425			
8061	W M U36C powered, 1980	145	175			
8062	C & S Burlington F-3 B dummy, 1980	150	225			
8062	Great Northern Steam, 1970		Not Manufactured			
8063	Seaboard SD-9 powered, 1980	125	175			
8064	F E C GP-9 powered, 1980	125	150			

		Exc	LN	Color	Cond	$
8065	F E C GP-9 dummy, 1980	80	100			
8066	T P & W GP-20 powered, 1980	100	125			
8067	T & P Alco A powered, 1980			Not Manufactured		
8071	Virginian SD-18 powered, 1980	100	150			
8072	Virginian SD-18 dummy, 1980	60	75			
(8100)	N & W Steam "611" 4-8-4, J-1, 1981	1000	1400			
(8101)	C & A Steam "659" 4-6-4, 1981	500	600			
8102	U P Steam 4-4-2, 1981-82	60	75			
(8104)	U P General 4-4-0, "3" J. C. Penney, 1981	300	395			
8111	D T & I NW-2 powered Switcher, 1971-74	35	75			
8140	Southern Steam 2-4-0, 1971	25	35			
8141	Pennsylvania Steam 2-4-2, 1971	40	55			
8142	C & O Steam 4-4-2, 1971	55	65			
8143	Milwaukee Steam 4-4-2, 1971	30	40			
(8150)	Penn GG-1 powered, green, 81	525	650			
8151	Burlington SD-28 powered, 81	125	175			
8152	C P SD-24 powered, 1981	195	250			
8153	R R NW-2 pow. Switcher, 1981	100	125			
8154	Alaska NW-2 powered Switcher, 1981-82	85	125			
8155	Monon U36B powered, 1981-82	75	100			
8156	Monon U36B dummy, 1981-82	60	75			
8157	Santa Fe Trainmaster, 1981	400	495			
8158	D M & I R GP-35 pow., 81-82	75	125			
8159	D M & I R GP-35 dum., 81-82	60	75			
8160	Burger King GP-20 pow., 81-82	90	120			
8161	L A S E R Gas Turbine, 1981-82	60	100			
8162	O N SD-18 powered, 1981	125	150			
8163	O N SD-18 dummy, 1981	100	125			
8164	Penn F-3 B unit, green, horn, 81	400	495			
8182	Nibco NW-2 pow. Switcher, 82	125	175			
8190	Diesel Horn Kit, 1981	—	35			
8200	(See 18200)					
8200	Kickapoo Dockside Steam 0-4-0, 1972	40	50			
8201	(See 18201)					
8203	Pennsylvania Steam 2-4-2, 1972	30	40			
8203	(See 18203)					
X 8204	C & O Steam 4-4-2, 1972	60	70			
8204	(See 18204)					
8206	N Y C Steam 4-6-4, 1972-74	225	275			
8206	(See 18206)					
8209	Pioneer Dockside Steam 0-4-0, 1972-76					
(A)	With four-wheel Tender	40	60			

		Exc	LN	Color Cond $
(B)	Without Tender	40	50	___ ___ ___
8210	Cowen Steam 4-6-4, 1982	425	500	___ ___ ___
8212	Black Cave Steam 0-4-0, 1982	30	50	___ ___ ___
8213	Rio Grande Steam 2-4-2, 82-83	60	70	___ ___ ___
8214	Pennsylvania Steam 2-4-2, 82-83	60	75	___ ___ ___
(8215)	Nickel Plate Steam 2-8-4, 1982	600	650	___ ___ ___
8250	S F GP-9 pow., 1972-75, 1982	90	120	___ ___ ___
8251-50	Horn/Whistle Controller, 72-74	2	3	___ ___ ___
8252	D & H Alco A unit pow., 1972	100	125	___ ___ ___
8253	D & H Alco B unit dummy, 72	50	75	___ ___ ___
8254	I C GP-9 dummy, 1972	60	75	___ ___ ___
8255	Santa Fe GP-9 dummy, 1972	60	75	___ ___ ___
8258	C N GP-7 dummy, 1972	65	80	___ ___ ___
8261	S P F-3 B unit dummy, 1982	700	1000	___ ___ ___
8260-8262	S P F-3 AA, sold as set	675	795	___ ___ ___
8263	Santa Fe GP-7 powered, 1982	75	100	___ ___ ___
8264	C P Snowplow, 1982	110	150	___ ___ ___
8265	Santa Fe SD-40 powered, 1982	325	425	___ ___ ___
8266	N & W SD-24 pow. w/horn, 82	150	200	___ ___ ___
8268	T & P Alco A unit pow., 82-83	75	90	___ ___ ___
8269	T & P Alco A unit dum., 82-83	30	50	___ ___ ___
8272	Pennsylvania EP-5, J. C. Penney 1982	275	350	___ ___ ___
8300	(See 18300)			
8300	Santa Fe Steam 2-4-0, 1976	20	25	___ ___ ___
8301	(See 18301)			
8302	Southern Steam 2-4-0, 1973-76	25	30	___ ___ ___
8302	(See 18302)			
8303	J C Steam 2-4-2, 1973-74	40	50	___ ___ ___
8303	See (18303)			
8304	B & O Steam 4-4-2, 1975	90	125	___ ___ ___
8304	C & O Steam 4-4-2, 1974-77	90	125	___ ___ ___
8304	Pennsylvania Steam 4-4-2, 1974	90	125	___ ___ ___
8304	Rock Island Steam 4-4-2, 73-74	100	150	___ ___ ___
8305	M R Steam 4-4-2, 1973	90	125	___ ___ ___
(8307)	Southern Pacific Steam 4-8-4, GS-4 "4449", 1983	1800	2200	___ ___ ___
8308	J C Steam 2-4-2, 1973-74	40	50	___ ___ ___
(8309)	Southern Steam 2-8-2 "4501" (FARR #4), 1984	425	550	___ ___ ___
8310	A T & S F Steam 2-4-0, 1974-75	30	40	___ ___ ___
8310	J C Steam 2-4-0, 1974-75	30	60	___ ___ ___
8310	Nickel Plate Steam 2-4-0, 74-75	30	60	___ ___ ___
8311	Southern Steam, 1973	30	40	___ ___ ___
8313	Santa Fe Steam 0-4-0, 1983	15	20	___ ___ ___
8314	Southern Steam 2-4-0, 1983	20	25	___ ___ ___
8315	B & O Steam 4-4-0, 1983	85	120	___ ___ ___
8350	U. S. Steel Gas Turbine, 1974-75	20	30	___ ___ ___

		Exc	LN	Color	Cond	$
8351	Santa Fe Alco A powered, 73-74	75	100			
8352	Santa Fe GP-20 powered, 73-75	60	100			
8353	Grand Trunk GP-7 pow., 1974-75	60	100			
8354	Erie NW-2 pow. Switcher, 73-75	90	120			
8355	S F GP-20 dum. w/horn, 73-75	80	125			
8356	Grand Trunk GP-7 dum., 74-75	40	60			
8357	Pennsylvania GP-9 pow., 73-75	125	150			
8358	Pennsylvania GP-9 dum., 73-75	60	100			
8359	Chessie GP-7 powered, 1973	100	150			
8360	Long Island GP-20 pow., 73-74	75	100			
8361	W P Alco A powered, 1973-74	100	125			
8362	W P Alco B dummy, 1973-74	50	75			
8363	B & O F-3 A, 1973-75	250	325			
8364	B & O F-3 A dummy, 1973-75	120	200			
8365/8366	C P F-3 AA set, 1973	500	850			
8367	Long Island GP-20 dummy with horn, 1973	75	90			
8368	Alaska R R Vulcan Switcher, 83	100	140			
8369	Erie-Lack. GP-20 powered, 1983	100	125			
8370/8371/8372	N Y C F-3 ABA, 83	500	700			
8374	Burlington NW-2 Switcher, 1983	90	125			
8375	C & N W GP-7 powered, 1983	100	125			
8376	U P SD-40, Magnetraction, 83	450	550			
8377	U. S. Switcher w/decal sheet, 83	60	100			
(8378)	Wab. "530" J. C. Penney, 83	1200	1500			
8379	Penn Motorized Fire Fighter, 85	140	175			
8380	Lionel Lines SD-28 pow., 1983	150	250			
8400	(See 18400)					
8402	Reading Steam 4-4-2, 1984	60	75			
8403	Chessie Steam 4-4-2, 1984-85	60	75			
(8404)	P R R 6-8-6, Steam, 1984-85	500	575			
8404	(See 18404)					
(8406)	N Y C Semi-scale Hudson Steam "783" 4-6-4, 1985	950	1100			
8410	Redwood Steam 4-4-0, 1984-85	40	60			
8452	Erie Alco A powered, 1974	80	100			
8453	Erie Alco B dummy, 1974	50	75			
8454	Rio Grande GP-7 pow., 1974-75	100	125			
8455	Rio Grande GP-7 dummy, 74-75	50	80			
8456	Norfolk Southern GP-7, 1974	60	75			
8458	Erie-Lackawanna SD-40 twin motors, 1985	375	450			
8459	R G Rotary Snowplow, 1984	100	135			
8460	M K T NW-2 powered Switcher, 1973-75	50	75			
8463	Chessie GP-20 powered, 1974	125	150			
8464/8465	Rio Grande F-3 AA set, 74	200	350			
8466/8467	Amtrak F-3 AA, 1974-75	—	500			

		Exc	LN	Color	Cond	$
8468	B & O F-3 B dummy, 1974	150	175			
8469	C P F-3 B dummy, 1974	200	300			
8470	Chessie U36B powered, 1974	100	150			
8471	Penn NW-2 pow. Switch., 73-74	250	300			
8473	Coca-Cola NW-2 powered Switcher,					
	1975	125	150			
8474	Rio Grande F-3 dummy, 1975	125	175			
8475	Amtrak F-3 B dummy, 1975	125	150			
8477	N Y C GP-9 powered, 1985	300	395			
8480/8481/8482	U P F-3 ABA, 85	450	550			
8485	U. S. Marines NW-2 Switch., 84	75	100			
8490	(See 8690)					
8500	(See 18500)					
8500	Pennsylvania Steam 2-4-0, 1975	20	25			
8501	(See 18501)					
8502	Santa Fe Steam 2-4-0, 1975	20	25			
8503	(See 18503)					
8504	(See 18504)					
8506	P R R Steam 0-4-0, 1975-77	100	150			
8507	A T S F Steam 2-4-0, 1975	25	30			
8512	S F Steam 0-4-0, blue, 1985-86	25	35			
8516	N Y C Steam 0-4-0, 1985-86	125	150			
8550	Jersey Central GP-9 pow., 1975	100	125			
8551	Pennsylvania EP-5 pow., 75-76	200	300			
8552/8553/8554	S P Alco ABA, 75-76	250	350			
8555/8557	M R F-3 AA, 1975	300	400			
8556	Chessie NW-2 powered Switcher,					
	1975-76	225	300			
8558	M R EP-5, powered, 1976	175	200			
8559	N & W GP-9 (see 1776)					
8560	Chessie U36B dummy, 1975	75	100			
8561	Jersey Central GP-9 dum., 75-76	60	80			
8562	MoPac GP-20 powered, 1975-76	100	125			
8563	Rock Island Alco A pow., 1975	75	100			
8564	Union Pacific U36B pow., 1975	125	175			
8565	MoPac GP-20 dummy, 1975-76	60	75			
8566	Southern F-3 A pow., 1975-77	275	400			
8567	Southern F-3 A dummy, 75-77	125	200			
8568	Preamble Exp. F-3 A pow., 75	100	150			
8569	SOO NW-2 pow. Switch., 75-77	75	100			
8570	Liberty Spec. Alco A pow., 75	75	100			
8571	Frisco U36B powered, 1975-76	75	100			
8572	Frisco U36B dummy, 1975-76	60	75			
8573	U P U36B dummy, 1975	200	275			
8575	Milwaukee Road F-3 B dum., 75	100	175			
8576	Penn GP-7 powered, 1975-76	125	150			
8578	N Y C Ballast Tamper powered,					
	1985, 1987	100	125			

	Exc	LN	Color	Cond	$
8580/8582 I C F-3 AA, 1985-87	400	475			
8581 I C F-3 B with horn, 1985, 87	200	250			
8585 B N SD-40 with twin motors, horn, 1985	350	450			
(8587) Wabash GP-9 (J. C. Penney Special), "484", 1985	300	395			
8600 N Y C Steam 4-6-4, 1976	250	300			
8601 Rock Island Steam 0-4-0, 76-77	20	25			
8601 (See 18601)					
8602 Rio Grande Steam 2-4-0, 76-78	25	30			
8602 (See 18602)					
8603 C & O Steam 4-6-4, 1976-77	175	275			
8604 Jersey Central Steam 2-4-2, 1976	40	45			
8604 (See 18604)					
(8606) Boston & Albany "784" Hudson, 4-6-4, 1986	1500	2150			
8606 N Y C 2-6-4 (see 18606)					
8607 (See 18607)					
8608 (See 18608)					
8609 (See 18609)					
(8610) Wabash Steam "672" 4-6-2, 1986-87	500	650			
8610 (See 18610)					
8611 (See 18611)					
8612 (See 18612)					
(8615) Berkshire Steam 2-8-4, J. C. Penney, "1970", Big Emma, 1986	950	1200			
8615 G T W (see 18615)					
8616 A T & S F Steam 4-4-2, 1986	65	75			
8616 (See 18616)					
8617 N K P Steam 4-4-2, 1986	65	75			
8618 (See 18618)					
8620 (See 18620)					
8625 Penn. Steam 2-4-0, 1986	25	35			
(8630) W & A 4-4-0, General, 1986	—	135			
8635 A T & S F Steam 0-4-0, 1986	120	145			
8650 B N U36B powered, 1976-77	125	150			
8651 B N U36B dummy, 1976-77	90	100			
8652 Santa Fe F-3 A pow., 1976-77	300	400			
8653 Santa Fe F-3 A dummy, 1976-77	225	350			
8654 Boston & Maine GP-9 pow., 76	115	150			
8655 Boston & Maine GP-9 dum., 76	80	100			
8656/8657/8658 C N Alco ABA, 1976	325	500			
8656 C N Alco A unit powered, 1976	150	200			
8657 C N Alco B dum. unit only, 76	75	100			
8658 C N Alco A dum. unit only, 76	100	200			
8659 Virginian Rectifier, 1976-77	125	175			
8660 C P Rail NW-2 Switcher, 76-77	100	125			

		Exc	LN	Color	Cond	$
8661	Southern F-3 B dummy	125	200	___	___	___
8662	B & O GP-7, 1986	100	125	___	___	___
8664	Amtrak Alco A powered, 76-77	100	150	___	___	___
8665	(See 1776)					
8666	Northern Pacific GP-9 pow., 76	125	150	___	___	___
8667	Amtrak Alco B dum., 1976-77	75	100	___	___	___
8668	N P GP-9 dummy, 1976	100	125	___	___	___
8669	I C U36B powered, 1976	125	150	___	___	___
8670	Chessie Gas Turbine, 1976	35	65	___	___	___
8679	Northern Pacific GP-20, 1986	100	125	___	___	___
8687	Jersey Central FM Diesel, 1986	360	525	___	___	___
(8690)	Lionel Lines Trolley Car, 1986	100	125	___	___	___
8700	(See 18700)					
(8701)	W & A R R (General) 4-4-0 "#3", 1977	150	200	___	___	___
8702	Crescent Limited Steam 4-6-4, 1977	375	475	___	___	___
8702	(See 18702)					
8703	Wabash Steam 2-4-2, 1977	25	35	___	___	___
8704	(See 18704)					
8705	(See 18705)					
8706	(See 18706)					
8707	(See 18707)					
8716	(See 18716)					
8750	The Rock GP-7 powered, 1977	100	125	___	___	___
8751	The Rock GP-7 dummy, 1977	50	75	___	___	___
8753	Penn GG-1, tuscan, 1977	500	600	___	___	___
8754	New Haven Rectifier, 1977-78	150	200	___	___	___
8755	S F U36B powered, 1977-78	150	200	___	___	___
8756	Santa Fe U36B dummy, 1977-78	90	100	___	___	___
8757	Conrail GP-9 powered, 1977-78	100	140	___	___	___
8758	Southern GP-7 dummy, 1978	80	100	___	___	___
8759	Erie-Lack. GP-9 pow., 1977-79	120	150	___	___	___
8760	Erie-Lack. GP-9 dum., 1977-79	100	125	___	___	___
8761	G T W NW-2 powered Switcher, 1977-78	125	175	___	___	___
8762	Great Northern EP-5, 1977-78	200	275	___	___	___
8763	N & W GP-9 powered, 1977-78	100	125	___	___	___
8764	B & O Budd RDC pow., 1977	125	175	___	___	___
8765	B & O Budd RDC dummy, 1977	100	125	___	___	___
8766	B & O Budd RDC powered with 8767, 8768, 1977	300	450	___	___	___
8767	B & O RDC dummy, 1977 (see 8766)					
8768	B & O RDC dummy, 1977 (see 8766)					
8769	Republic Steel Gas Turbine, 1977	20	40	___	___	___
8770	E M D NW-2 pow. Switcher, 77	100	125	___	___	___
8771	G N U36B powered, 1977	100	120	___	___	___
8772	G M & O GP-20 powered, 1977	100	120	___	___	___

		Exc	LN	Color	Cond	$
8773	Mickey Mouse U36B powered, 1977-78	400	500			
8774	Southern GP-7 powered, 77-78	125	150			
8775	L V GP-9 pow., 1977-78	125	150			
8776	C & N W GP-20 pow., 1977-78	125	150			
8777	S F F-3 B unit dummy, 1977-78	200	300			
8778	L V GP-9 dummy, 1977-78	80	100			
8779	C & N W GP-20 dum., 1977-78	80	100			
8800	(See 18800)					
8800	L L Steam 4-4-2, 1978-81	100	125			
8801	(See 18801)					
8801	Blue Comet Steam 4-6-4, 79-80	400	500			
8802	(See 18802)					
8803	Santa Fe Steam 0-4-0, 1979	10	20			
8804	(See 18804)					
8805	(See 18805, 18890)					
8806	(See 18806)					
8807	(See 18807)					
8808	(See 18808)					
8809	(See 18809)					
8810	(See 18810)					
8811	(See 18811)					
8813	(See 18813)					
8814	(See 18814)					
8815	(See 18815)					
8850	Penn Central GG-1, black, 1979	375	475			
8851/8852	N H F-3, AA, pr., 1978-79	300	400			
8854	C P Rail GP-9 powered, 78-79	85	125			
8855	M R SD-18 powered, 1978	115	150			
8857	N P U36B powered, 1978-80	100	125			
8858	N P U36B dummy, 1978-80	55	85			
8859	Conrail Rectifier, 1978-80, 1982	150	195			
8860	Rock NW-2 pow. Switch., 78-79	100	125			
8861	Santa Fe Alco A pow., 1978-79	75	100			
8862	Santa Fe Alco A dummy, 78-79	40	50			
8864	New Haven F-3 B unit, 1978	125	175			
8866	M & St L GP-9 powered, 1978	100	125			
8867	M & St L GP-9 dummy, 1978	75	100			
8868	Amtrak Budd RDC pow., 78, 80	150	200			
8869	Amtrak Budd RDC dum., 78, 80	70	100			
8870	Amtrak Budd RDC dum., 78, 80	70	100			
8871	Amtrak Budd RDC dum., 78, 80	70	100			
8872	Santa Fe SD-18 powered, 78-79	100	150			
8873	Santa Fe SD-18 dummy, 1978-79	75	100			
8900	A T & S F Steam 4-6-4, 1979	350	425			
8900	(See 18900)					
8901	(See 18901)					
8902	(See 18902)					

		Exc	LN	Color	Cond	$
8902	A C L Steam 2-4-0, 1979-82	15	20			
8903	Rio Grande Steam 2-4-2, 1979	20	25			
8903	(See 18903)					
8904	Wabash Steam 2-4-2, 1979, 1981	35	40			
8904	(See 18904)					
8905	Steam (no letters) 0-4-0, 1979	10	20			
8906	(See 18906)					
8950	Virginian Trainmaster, 1978	350	495			
8951	S P Trainmaster, 1979	625	700			
8952/8953	Penn. F-3, AA, green, 79	600	750			
8955	Southern U36B powered, 1979	125	175			
8956	Southern U36B dummy, 1979	70	100			
8957	B N GP-20 powered, green, 79	100	125			
8958	B N GP-20 dummy, green, 79	80	100			
8960	S P U36C, powered, 1979	80	100			
8961	S P U36C dummy, 1979	60	75			
8962	Reading U36B, 1979	150	200			
8970/8971	Penn. F-3, AA, pair, 79-80	400	500			
8977	(See 18000)					
9001	Conrail Boxcar, 1986	12	15			
9010	Great Northern Hopper, blue, 1971	6	8			
9011	Great Northern Hopper, 1971, 79	6	8			
9012	T A & G Short Hop., 1971-72, 79	5	7			
9013	C N Hopper, red, 1972-74, 1979	4	5			
9014	Trailer Train Flatcar (O27), 1978	4	6			
9015	Reading Short Hopper, 73-74, 79	20	25			
9016	Chessie Short Hop., yellow, 75-79	4	6			
9017	C P Short Hopper, 1971	6	8			
9017	Wabash Gon. (O27), 1978, 80-81	4	5			
9018	D T & I Short Hopper, 1978, 81	5	7			
9019	Unlettered Set Flatcar (O27), 1978	3	4			
9020	U P Flatcar (O27), 1970-77	4	5			
9021	Santa Fe Work Caboose, 1970-74	10	15			
9022	A T & S F Bulkhead Flat., 71, 77	8	15			
9023	M K T Bulkhead Flatcar, 74, 78	8	12			
9024	C & O Flatcar, yellow (O27), 74	4	6			
9025	D T & I Work Cab., 1971-74, 78	8	10			
9026	Republic Steel Flatcar, 75-77, 80	6	8			
9027	SOO Work Caboose, 1975	8	10			
9029	B & O Flatcar, 1976	4	5			
9030	Kickapoo, 1972, 1979	5	7			
9031	Nickel Plate Gondola, 1974, 79, 83	5	7			
9032	S P Gondola (O27), 1975, 1978	3	4			
9033	P C Gondola, 1977, 79, 81-82	3	4			
9034	L L Leisure Short Hop. (O27), 77	35	50			
9035	Conrail Boxcar (O27), 1978-82	4	8			
9036	Mobilgas 1-D Tank, white, 78-80	6	12			
9037	Conrail Boxcar (O27), 1978-81	4	8			

		Exc	LN	Color	Cond	$
9038	Chessie Short Hopper, blue, 75-79	8	10	___	___	___
9039	Cheerios Boxcar (O27), 1971-72	6	8	___	___	___
9039	Mobilgas 1-D Tank, red, 1978, 80	10	15	___	___	___
9040	Wheaties Boxcar (O27), 1970	7	10	___	___	___
9041	Hershey's Boxcar (O27), 1971	10	15	___	___	___
9042	Autolite Boxcar (O27), 1972	8	12	___	___	___
9043	Erie-Lack. Boxcar (O27), 1973-74	8	12	___	___	___
9044	D & R G W Boxcar (O27), 75, 79	6	8	___	___	___
9045	Toys 'R Us Boxcar (O27)	40	50	___	___	___
9046	True Value Boxcar (O27), 1976	40	50	___	___	___
9047	Toys 'R Us Boxcar (O27)	35	50	___	___	___
9048	Toys 'R Us Boxcar (O27)	35	50	___	___	___
(9049)	Toys 'R Us Boxcar, 1979	35	50	___	___	___
9050	Sunoco 1-D Short Tank, 1970-71	20	25	___	___	___
9051	Firestone 1-D Tank, white, 74-75	15	20	___	___	___
9052	Toys 'R Us Short Boxcar, 1977	30	40	___	___	___
9053	True Value Short Boxcar	35	50	___	___	___
9054	J C Penney Short Boxcar	35	50	___	___	___
9055	Republic Steel Gon. (O27), 77-81	10	12	___	___	___
9057	C P Rail SP Caboose, 1978-79	9	11	___	___	___
9058	Lionel Lines SP Caboose, 1978-79	6	8	___	___	___
9059	Lionel Lines SP Caboose, 1979	8	10	___	___	___
9060	Nickel Plate SP Caboose, 1970-71	6	8	___	___	___
9061	A T & S F SP Caboose, 70-71, 78	6	8	___	___	___
9062	Penn Central SP Caboose, 1970-71	5	9	___	___	___
9063	G T W SP Caboose, 1970	20	25	___	___	___
9064	C & O SP Caboose, 1971	7	10	___	___	___
9065	C N SP Caboose, 1971-72	20	25	___	___	___
9066	Southern SP Caboose	8	10	___	___	___
9067	Kickapoo Valley Bobber Cab., 72	7	10	___	___	___
9068	Reading Bobber Caboose, 1973-75	6	8	___	___	___
9069	Jersey Central SP Caboose, 73-74	6	8	___	___	___
9070	Rock Island SP Caboose, 1973-74	10	15	___	___	___
9071	A T & S F Bobber Cab., 1974-75	8	10	___	___	___
9072	B & O SP Type VII, 1972-73	6	9	___	___	___
9073	Coca-Cola SP Caboose, 1973	10	15	___	___	___
9075	Rock Island SP Caboose, 1973-74	10	15	___	___	___
9076	We The People SP Caboose, 1975	20	40	___	___	___
9077	R G SP Caboose, 1977-79, 1981	6	8	___	___	___
9078	Rock Island Bobber Cab., 1977-79	6	8	___	___	___
9079	A T & S F Caboose, 1979		Not Manufactured			
9079	G T W Short Hopper, 1977	15	20	___	___	___
9080	Wabash SP Caboose, 1977	10	11	___	___	___
9085	A T & S F Work Caboose, 80-81	5	6	___	___	___
9090	Mini-Max four-whl. Van Car, 71	35	50	___	___	___
9100	Amtrak (see 19100)					
9100	Union Pacific GE-8 Locomotive (see 18205)					
9101	(See 19101)					

		Exc	LN	Color	Cond	$
9102	(See 19102)					
9103	(See 19103)					
9104	(See 19104)					
9105	(See 19105)					
9106	(See 19106)					
9106	Miller Vat Car, 1984	15	20	___	___	___
9107	Dr. Pepper Vat Carrier, 1986-87	15	20	___	___	___
9110	B & O Quad Hopper, 1971	25	35	___	___	___
9111	N & W Quad Hopper, 1972	10	20	___	___	___
9112	D & R G Quad Hopper, 1972-73	12	20	___	___	___
9113	N & W Quad Hopper, 1973	25	40	___	___	___
9114	Morton's Quad Hopper, 1975-76	15	25	___	___	___
9115	Planter's Quad Hopper, 1974-76	15	25	___	___	___
9116	Domino Sugar Quad Hop., 74-76	15	25	___	___	___
9117	Alaska Quad Hopper, 1974-76	15	25	___	___	___
9118	L C C A Corning Quad Hop., 74	75	90	___	___	___
9119	Detroit & Mack. Quad Hop., 75	25	30	___	___	___
9120	N P Flatcar w/vans, 1970-71	40	50	___	___	___
9121	L & N Flatcar with dozer, 1974, 1976, 1978-79	35	45	___	___	___
9122	N P Flatcar with vans, 1972-75	40	50	___	___	___
9123	C & O Auto Carrier, 1974	15	30	___	___	___
9123	T C A Dearborn Auto Carrier, 73	45	55	___	___	___
9124	P & L E Flatcar with logs, 1973	10	15	___	___	___
9125	N & W Auto Carrier, 1974	30	40	___	___	___
9126	C & O Auto Carrier, 1973-74	15	25	___	___	___
9128	Heinz Vat Car, 1974-76	15	20	___	___	___
9129	N & W Auto Carrier, brown, 75	30	45	___	___	___
9130	B & O Quad Hopper, 1970-71	15	20	___	___	___
9131	Rio Grande Gondola, orange, 1974	5	8	___	___	___
9132	Libby's Vat Car, 1975-77	15	20	___	___	___
9133	B N Flatcar w/van, green, 76, 80	30	50	___	___	___
9134	Virginian Quad Hopper, 1976-77	20	25	___	___	___
9135	N & W Quad Hopper, blue, 1971	15	20	___	___	___
9136	Republic Steel Gon., blue, 76-79	8	10	___	___	___
9138	Sunoco 3-D Tank, black, 1978	35	45	___	___	___
9139	P C Auto Carrier, green, 1977	20	30	___	___	___
9140	Burlington Gondola, 70-71, 80-81	10	12	___	___	___
9141	B N Gondola 1970-71, 1980-81	6	8	___	___	___
9142	Republic Steel Gondola, green, 71	6	8	___	___	___
9143	Canadian National Gondola, 1973	40	50	___	___	___
9144	Rio Grande Gondola, black, 1974	6	8	___	___	___
9145	I C Gulf Auto Carrier, orange, 77	20	35	___	___	___
9146	Mogen David Vat Car, 1977-79	15	20	___	___	___
9147	Texaco 1-D Tank, chrome, 1977	20	40	___	___	___
9148	Dupont 3-D Tank, 1977-79, 1981	20	25	___	___	___
9149	C P Rail Flatcar with vans, 1977	20	40	___	___	___
9150	Gulf 1-D Tank Car, white, 70-71	30	35	___	___	___

		Exc	LN	Color	Cond	$
9151	Shell 1-D Tank Car, yellow, 1972	25	30			
9152	Shell 1-D Tank Car, 1973-74	20	25			
9153	Chevron 1-D Tank Car, 1974-76	15	30			
9154	Borden 1-D Tank, chrome, 75-76	30	40			
9155	L C C A Monsanto 1-D Tank,75	65	75			
9156	Mobilgas 1-D Tank Car, 1976-77	30	40			
9157	C & O Flatcar w/crane, 76-78, 81	35	40			
9158	P C Flatcar w/shovel, 76-77, 80	35	40			
9159	Sunoco 1-D Tank Car, silver, 75	40	60			
9160	I C N5C Caboose, 1970-72	25	35			
9161	C N N5C Caboose, 1971-72	15	35			
9162	P R R N5C Caboose, 1972-76	35	45			
9163	A T & S F N5C Caboose, 73-76	15	25			
9165	C P N5C Caboose, 1973	25	40			
9166	Rio Grande SP Caboose, 1974	20	25			
9167	Chessie N5C Caboose, 1974-76	40	50			
9168	Union Pacific N5C Cab., 1975-76	20	30			
9169	Milwaukee Road SP Cab., 1975	15	20			
9170	N & W (see 1776, 1976)					
9171	MoPac SP Caboose, 1975-77	15	20			
9172	Penn Central SP Caboose, 75-77	25	35			
9173	Jersey Central SP Caboose, 75-77	15	20			
9174	P & L E B/W Cab., green, 1976	75	90			
9175	Virginian N5C Caboose, 1975-77	20	30			
9176	B A R N5C Caboose, 1976	20	35			
9177	N P B/W Caboose, green, 1976	25	35			
9178	Illinois Central SP Caboose	20	25			
9179	Chessie Bobber Caboose, 1979	6	10			
9180	The Rock N5C Cab., 1977-78	20	40			
9181	B & M N5C Caboose, blue, 1977	15	25			
9182	N & W N5C Cab., black, 77-80	15	35			
9183	Mickey Mouse N5C Cab., 77-78	35	50			
9184	Erie Bay Window Cab., 1977-78	20	30			
9185	G T W N5C Caboose, 1977	20	35			
9186	Conrail N5C Caboose, 1977-78	30	40			
9187	G M & O SP Caboose, 1977-78	15	30			
9188	G N B/W Caboose, blue, 1977	30	40			
9189	Gulf 1-D Tank Car, chrome, 1977	35	45			
9189	Norfolk Southern NC5 Cab., 74	12	15			
9193	Budweiser Vat Car, 1983	15	20			
9195	Rolling Stock Asst. (O27), 88	NRS	NRS			
9200	Illinois Central Boxcar, 1970-72	25	35			
9201	Penn Central Boxcar, 1970	20	30			
9202	Santa Fe Boxcar, red, 1970	30	40			
9203	Union Pacific Boxcar, 1970	35	45			
9204	N P Boxcar, green, 1970	30	35			
9205	Norfolk & Western Boxcar, 1970	20	25			
9206	G N Boxcar, blue, 1970-71	20	25			

		Exc	LN	Color	Cond	$
9207	SOO Boxcar, red, 1971	20	25			
9208	C P Rail Boxcar, yellow, 1971-72	20	25			
9209	B N Boxcar, green, 1970-72	20	25			
9210	B & O Automobile Boxcar, 1971	20	30			
9211	Penn Central Boxcar, 1971	30	35			
9212	L C C A S C L Flatcar T O F C, Atlanta, 1976	35	40			
9213	M & St L Quad Hopper, 1978	25	35			
9214	N P Box., tuscan, 1970-72	30	40			
9215	Norfolk & Western Boxcar, 1971	30	35			
9216	G N Auto Carrier, 1978	25	40			
9217	SOO Lines Oper. Box, 82-83, 85	15	25			
9218	Monon Operating Boxcar, 81-82	15	25			
9219	M P Operating Boxcar, 1983	25	35			
9220	Borden Oper. Milk Car Set, 85-86	90	100			
9221	Poultry Dispatch, 1985-86	35	40			
9222	L & N Flatcar with vans, 1983	15	25			
9223	Reading Operating Boxcar, 1985	25	30			
9224	Louisville Oper. Horse Car Set, 85	75	90			
9225	Conrail Oper. Barrel Car, 84-85	35	50			
9226	D & H Flatcar with vans, 1985	20	30			
9228	Canadian Pacific Boxcar, 1986	20	30			
9229	Express Mail Oper. Boxcar, 85-86	25	35			
9230	Monon Boxcar, brown, 1972	12	15			
9231	Reading B/W Caboose, 1979	30	40			
9232	Allis Chalmers Flatcar w/load, 80	35	60			
9233	Die-cast Transformer Flatcar, 80	60	85			
9234	Radioactive Waste Car, 1980	30	45			
9235	U P Flatcar with derrick, 1983	10	15			
9236	C & N W Derrick Car, 1985	15	20			
9237	U P S Operating Boxcar, 1984		Not Manufactured			
9238	N P Operating Log Dump, 1985	15	20			
9239	Lionel Lines N5C Caboose, 1985	60	80			
9240	N Y C Oper. Hopper Car, 1986	30	40			
9241	Penn Oper. Log Dump Car, 85-86	15	20			
9245	Illinois Central Derrick Car, 1985		Not Manufactured			
(9247)	N Y C Searchlight Car (See 6529)		Not Manufactured			
9250	Waterpoxy 3-D Tank Car, 1971	25	50			
X9259	L C C A Southern B/W Caboose, 1977	35	40			
9260	Reynolds Quad Hopper, 1975-78	12	20			
9261	Sunmaid Quad Hopper, 1975-76	15	20			
9262	Ralston-Purina Quad Hop., 75-76	60	90			
9263	Pennsylvania Quad, 1975-77	30	40			
9264	Ill. Central Quad Hopper, 1975-77	25	30			
9265	W M Chessie Quad Hop., 75-77	25	30			
9266	Southern "Big John" Quad, 1976	50	75			
9267	Alcoa Quad Hopper, 1975	30	40			

		Exc	LN	Color	Cond	$
9268	N P B/W Caboose, black, 77-78	30	40			
9269	M R B/W Caboose, 1978	35	60			
9270	N P N5C Caboose, 1978, 1980	15	25			
9271	M & St L B/W Caboose, 78-79	20	30			
9272	N H B/W Caboose, 1978-80	15	25			
9273	Southern B/W Caboose, 1978	40	55			
9274	Santa Fe B/W Caboose, red, 1978	60	90			
9276	Peabody Open Quad Hopper, 78	25	35			
9276	T & P SP Caboose, 1980			Not Manufactured		
9277	Cities Service 3-D Tank Car, 77	40	50			
9278	Lifesavers 1-D Tank Car, 78-79	80	100			
9279	Magnolia 3-D Tank Car, 1978-79	20	25			
9280	A T & S F Horse Trans., 78-80	15	20			
9281	A T S F 2-level carrier, 1978-79	20	30			
9282	G N Flat. w/vans, 1978, 1981-82	30	45			
9283	Union Pacific Gondola, 1977	8	10			
9284	A T & S F Gondola, red, 77-78	20	25			
9285	I C Gulf Flatcar w/vans, 1977	50	65			
9286	B & L E Quad Hopper, 1977	15	25			
9287	Southern N5C Caboose, 1978	15	25			
9288	L V N5C Cab., 1978, 1980	20	30			
9289	C & N W N5C Caboose, 78, 80	20	30			
9290	U P Operating Barrel Car, 1983	55	85			
9300	P C Dump Car, green, 1970-73	15	20			
9301	Operating U. S. Mail Car, 1975-83	20	30			
9302	L & N Searchlight Car, 1973-74	12	17			
9303	U P Oper. Log Dump, 1974, 79	10	15			
9304	C & O Coal Oper. Dump, 73-76	10	12			
9305	S F Animated Stock, 1980, 1982	15	20			
9306	A T S F Flatcar, 1980	15	20			
9307	Erie Animated Gon., 1979-83, 85	40	60			
9308	Aquarium Car, 1981-83, 1985	75	85			
9309	T P & W B/W Caboose, 1980-81	25	35			
9310	A T & S F Log Dump, 1978-79, 1981-82	10	15			
9311	U P Oper. Coal Dump, 1978-82	10	15			
9312	Conrail Searchlight Car, 1978-83	15	20			
9313	Gulf 3-D Tank Car, black, 1979	45	55			
9315	Southern Pacific Gondola, 1979	20	30			
9316	S P B/W Caboose, 1979	60	85			
9317	A T & S F B/W Cab., blue, 1979	25	35			
9319	T C A Silver Jubilee Gold Bullion Car, 1979	250	325			
9320	Fort Knox Gold Bullion Car, 79	175	250			
9321	A T & S F 1-D Tank (FARR #1), 1979	30	40			
9322	A T & S F Quad Hopper (FARR #1), 1979	70	80			

		Exc	LN	Color	Cond	$
9323	A T & S F B/W Cab., brown, 79	30	45	___	___	___
9324	Tootsie Roll 1-D Tank, 79, 81-82	35	45	___	___	___
9325	(See 9363, 9364)					
9325	N & W Flat. w/fence, black, 80-81	5	10	___	___	___
9325	N & W Flat. w/cab, red, 78-79	5	10	___	___	___
9326	B N B/W Caboose, green, 79-80	20	25	___	___	___
9327	Bakelite 1-D Tank Car, 1980	15	20	___	___	___
9328	W M Chessie B/W Caboose, 80	30	50	___	___	___
9329	W M Chessie Crane, 1980	45	70	___	___	___
9330	Kickapoo Valley Dump Car, 1972	3	8	___	___	___
9331	Union 76 1-D Tank Car, 1979	40	60	___	___	___
9332	Reading Crane, 1979	40	55	___	___	___
9333	S P Flatcar with vans, 1980	40	50	___	___	___
9334	Humble 1-D Tank Car, 1979	20	30	___	___	___
9335	B & O Oper. Log Dump, 1986	15	20	___	___	___
9336	C P Rail Gondola, 1979	20	25	___	___	___
9338	Penn Power Quad Hopper, 1979	50	75	___	___	___
9339	G N Boxcar (O27), 1979-81, 1983	7	10	___	___	___
9340	I C Gondola (O27), 1979-81	5	10	___	___	___
9341	A C L SP Cab., 1979-82, 1986-90	6	8	___	___	___
9344	Citgo 3-D Tank, 1980	35	50	___	___	___
9345	Reading Searchlight Car, 1985	20	25	___	___	___
9346	Wabash SP Caboose, 1979	6	10	___	___	___
9347	T T O S Niagara Falls 3-D Tank Car, 1979	40	50	___	___	___
9348	Santa Fe Crane, 1979	55	70	___	___	___
9349	San Francisco Mint, 1980	110	150	___	___	___
9351	Pennsylvania Auto Carrier, 1980	20	40	___	___	___
9352	C & N W Flatcar w/vans, 1980	60	85	___	___	___
9353	Crystal 3-D Tank Car, 1980	15	25	___	___	___
9354	Pennzoil 1-D Tank Car, 1981	20	30	___	___	___
9355	D & H B/W Caboose, 1980	20	25	___	___	___
9356	Life Savers Stik-O-Pep Tank, 80			Not Manufactured		
9357	Smokey Mountain Bob. Cab., 79	8	10	___	___	___
9358	L C C A Sands of Iowa Quad Hopper, 1980	30	40	___	___	___
9359	National Basketball Boxcar, 1980	20	30	___	___	___
9360	National Hockey League Box., 80	20	30	___	___	___
9361	C & N W B/W Caboose, 1980	45	60	___	___	___
9362	Major League Baseball Box., 80	20	30	___	___	___
9363	N & W Operating Dump, 1979	5	8	___	___	___
9364	N & W Crane Car, 1978	8	10	___	___	___
9365	Toys 'R Us Boxcar (O27), 1979	40	50	___	___	___
9366	U P Quad Hop. (FARR #2), 80	25	35	___	___	___
9367	U P 1-D Tank (FARR #2), 1980	30	40	___	___	___
9368	U P B/W Cab. (FARR #2), 80	30	45	___	___	___
9369	Sinclair 1-D Tank Car, 1980	45	60	___	___	___
9370	Seaboard Gondola, 1980	20	25	___	___	___

		Exc	LN	Color	Cond	$
9371	Lantic Sugar Quad Hopper, 1980	25	35	___	___	___
9372	Seaboard B/W Caboose, 1980	30	40	___	___	___
9373	Getty 1-D Tank, white, 1980-81	40	50	___	___	___
9374	Reading Quad Hopper, 1980-81	60	75	___	___	___
9376	T & P SP Caboose, 1981	20	25	___	___	___
9378	Lionel Flatcar w/yel. derrick, 81	15	20	___	___	___
9379	A T & S F Gondola, black, 1980	25	35	___	___	___
9379	Lionel Flatcar w/derrick, 1980			Not Manufacture
9380	N Y N H & H SP Caboose, 1980	10	12	___	___	___
9381	Chessie SP Caboose, 1980	8	10	___	___	___
9382	Florida East Coast B/W Cab., 80	25	35	___	___	___
9383	U P Flat. w/vans (FARR #2), 80	30	40	___	___	___
9384	G N Oper. Short Hopper, 1981	55	75	___	___	___
9385	Alaska Gondola, yellow, 1981	30	40	___	___	___
9386	Pure Oil 1-D Tank Car, 1981	40	50	___	___	___
9387	Burlington B/W Caboose, red, 81	35	45	___	___	___
9388	Toys 'R Us Boxcar (O27), 1981	40	50	___	___	___
9389	Radioactive Waste Car, 1981	30	40	___	___	___
9398	Penn Operating Coal Dump, 1983	20	25	___	___	___
9399	C & N W Coal Dump, 1983-84	15	20	___	___	___
9400	Conrail Boxcar, brown, 1978	15	20	___	___	___
9401	Great Northern Boxcar, 1979	15	20	___	___	___
9402	Susquehanna Boxcar, 1978	30	35	___	___	___
9403	S C L Boxcar, black, 1978	15	20	___	___	___
9404	Nickel Plate Boxcar, 1978-79	30	40	___	___	___
9405	Chattahoochie Boxcar, 1978-79	15	20	___	___	___
9406	D & R G W Boxcar, 1978-79	15	20	___	___	___
9407	Union Pacific Cattle Car, 1978	25	35	___	___	___
9408	Lionel Lines Circus Car, 1978	30	40	___	___	___
9411	Lackawanna "Snow" Boxcar, 78	50	60	___	___	___
9412	R F & P Boxcar, 1979	12	18	___	___	___
9413	Napierville Jct. Boxcar, 1979-80	10	15	___	___	___
9414	Cotton Belt Boxcar, 1980	15	20	___	___	___
9414	L O T S Cotton Belt Box., 1980	—	35	___	___	___
9415	P & W Boxcar, 1979	10	15	___	___	___
9416	M D & W Boxcar, 1979, 1981	10	15	___	___	___
9417	C P Rail Boxcar, gold/black, 80	35	45	___	___	___
9418	F A R R Boxcar, 1979	75	90	___	___	___
9419	U P Boxcar (FARR #2), 1980	25	35	___	___	___
9420	B & O "Sentinel" Boxcar, 1980	25	35	___	___	___
9421	Maine Central Boxcar, 1980	12	20	___	___	___
9422	E J & E Boxcar, 1980	15	25	___	___	___
9423	N Y N H & H Boxcar, 1980	20	35	___	___	___
9424	T P & W Boxcar, orange, 1980	15	20	___	___	___
9425	British Columbia Auto Boxcar, 80	20	25	___	___	___
9426	Chesapeake & Ohio Boxcar, 1980	20	35	___	___	___
9427	Bay Line Boxcar, 1980-81	10	20	___	___	___
9428	T P & W Boxcar, green, 1980	35	50	___	___	___

		Exc	LN	Color	Cond	$
9429	The Early Years Boxcar, 1980	25	30	___	___	___
9430	Standard Gauge Years Boxcar, 80	25	30	___	___	___
9431	The Prewar Years Boxcar, 1980	25	30	___	___	___
9432	The Postwar Years Boxcar, 1980	85	125	___	___	___
9433	The Golden Years Boxcar, 1980	85	125	___	___	___
9434	Joshua Lionel Cowen Boxcar, 80	70	100	___	___	___
9435	L C C A Central of Georgia Boxcar, 1981	40	50	___	___	___
9436	Burlington Boxcar, red, 1981	40	50	___	___	___
9437	Northern Pacific Cattle Car, 1981	30	50	___	___	___
9438	Ontario Northland Boxcar, 1981	20	25	___	___	___
9439	Ashley Drew & Northern Box., 81	10	20	___	___	___
9440	Reading Boxcar, 1981	40	70	___	___	___
9441	Pennsylvania Boxcar, 1981	40	70	___	___	___
9442	Canadian Pacific Boxcar, 1981	15	20	___	___	___
9443	F E C Boxcar, 1981	15	20	___	___	___
9444	Louisiana Midland Boxcar, 1981	15	20	___	___	___
9445	Vermont Northern Boxcar, 1981	15	20	___	___	___
9446	Sabine River Boxcar, 1981	15	20	___	___	___
9447	Pullman Standard Boxcar, 1981	15	20	___	___	___
9448	A T & S F Cattle Car, brown, 81	40	55	___	___	___
9449	G N Box., green (FARR #3), 81	35	50	___	___	___
9450	G N Cattle, red (FARR #3), 1981	75	100	___	___	___
9451	Southern Boxcar (FARR #4), 84	40	55	___	___	___
9452	Western Pacific Boxcar, 1982-83	15	20	___	___	___
9453	M P A Boxcar, 1982-83	10	15	___	___	___
9454	New Hope & Ivyland Box., 82-83	10	15	___	___	___
9455	Milwaukee Road Boxcar, 1982-83	15	20	___	___	___
9456	P R R Auto Box. (FARR #5), 85	35	50	___	___	___
9460	L C C A D & T S L Box., 1982	35	60	___	___	___
9461	Norfolk & Southern Boxcar, 83	35	55	___	___	___
9462	Southern Pacific Boxcar, 83-84	20	25	___	___	___
9463	Texas & Pacific Boxcar, 1983-84	12	15	___	___	___
9464	N C & St L Boxcar, 1983-84	12	15	___	___	___
9465	A T & S F Boxcar, green, 1983	12	25	___	___	___
9466	Wanamaker Boxcar, 1982	90	120	___	___	___
9467	Tenn. World's Fair Boxcar, 1982	35	45	___	___	___
9468	U P Auto Boxcar, red, 1983	40	50	___	___	___
9469	N Y C Pacemaker Boxcar (Standard O), 1985	110	125	___	___	___
9470	Chicago Beltline Boxcar, 1984	15	20	___	___	___
9471	Atlantic Coast Line Boxcar, 1984	15	20	___	___	___
9472	Detroit & Mackinac Boxcar, 1985	20	25	___	___	___
9473	Lehigh Valley Boxcar, 1984	15	20	___	___	___
9474	Erie-Lackawanna Boxcar, 1985	45	55	___	___	___
9475	D & H "I Love N Y" Box., 84-85	25	40	___	___	___
9476	Pennsylvania Boxcar (FARR #5), 1985	40	50	___	___	___

		Exc	LN	Color	Cond	$
9480	M N & S Boxcar, 1985-86	15	20			
9481	Seaboard System Boxcar, 85-86	15	20			
9482	Norfolk Southern Boxcar, 85-86	15	20			
9483	Manufacturers Railway Boxcar, 1985-86	12	15			
9484	Lionel 85th Anniv. Boxcar, 1985	20	30			
9486	"I Love Michigan" Boxcar, 1986	15	20			
9491	Christmas Car, 1986	35	40			
9492	Lionel Lines Boxcar, 1986	30	50			
9500	Milwaukee Road Pullman, 1973	40	60			
9501	Milwaukee Road Pullman, 1973	30	40			
9502	Milwaukee Road Observation, 73	40	60			
9503	Milwaukee Road Pullman 1974	40	60			
9504	Milwaukee Road Pullman, 1974	30	40			
9505	Milwaukee Road Pullman, 1974	30	40			
9506	Milwaukee Road Baggage, 1975	25	40			
9507	Pennsylvania Pullman, 1974	40	60			
9508	Pennsylvania Pullman, 1974	40	60			
9509	Pennsylvania Observation, 1974	50	75			
9510	Pennsylvania Combine, 1975	30	50			
9511	Milwaukee Road Pullman, 1974	30	50			
9512	T T O S Summerdale Junction coach, 1974	40	50			
9513	Pennsylvania Pullman, 1975	30	50			
9514	Pennsylvania Pullman, 1975	30	50			
9515	Pennsylvania Pullman, 1975	30	50			
9516	Baltimore & Ohio Pullman, 1975	25	40			
9517	Baltimore & Ohio Coach, 1975	40	60			
9518	Baltimore & Ohio Obs., 1975	40	60			
9519	Baltimore & Ohio Combine, 1975	40	60			
9520	T T O S Phoenix combine, 1975	40	50			
9521	Pennsylvania Baggage, 1975	100	125			
9522	Milwaukee Road Baggage, 1975	100	125			
9523	Baltimore & Ohio Baggage, 1975	60	85			
9524	Baltimore & Ohio Pullman, 1976	30	50			
9525	Baltimore & Ohio Pullman, 1976	30	50			
9526	T T O S Snowbird Obs., 1976	40	50			
9527	Milwaukee Campaign, 1976	50	65			
9528	Pennsylvania Campaign, 1976	60	75			
9529	B & O Campaign, 1976	55	60			
9530	Southern Baggage, 1978	30	50			
9531	Southern Combine, 1978	30	50			
9532	Southern Pullman, 1978	30	50			
9533	Southern Pullman, 1978	30	50			
9534	Southern Observation, 1978	30	50			
9535	T T O S Columbus Pullman, 1977	40	50			
9536	Blue Comet Baggage, 1978	30	50			
9537	Blue Comet Combine, 1978	30	50			

		Exc	LN	Color	Cond	$
538	Blue Comet Pullman, 1978	30	60	___	___	___
539	Blue Comet Pullman, 1978	30	60	___	___	___
540	Blue Comet Observation, 1978	30	50	___	___	___
541	Santa Fe Baggage, 1980, 1982	20	30	___	___	___
542	Baltimore & Ohio Pullman, 1976	30	50	___	___	___
544	T C A Chicago Obs., 1980	—	75	___	___	___
545	U P Baggage, 1985	75	100	___	___	___
546	U P Combine, 1985	75	100	___	___	___
547	U P Observation, 1985	75	100	___	___	___
548	U P "Placid Bay" Coach, 1985	75	100	___	___	___
549	U P "Ocean Sunset" Coach, 1985	75	100	___	___	___
551	W & A Baggage, 1977-79	30	50	___	___	___
552	W & A Coach	30	50	___	___	___
553	W & A Flatcar w/fences, 78-79	15	20	___	___	___
554	Alton Limited Baggage, 1981	40	60	___	___	___
555	Alton Limited Combine, 1981	40	60	___	___	___
556	Alton Limited Coach, 1981	50	80	___	___	___
557	Alton Limited Coach, 1981	50	80	___	___	___
558	Alton Limited Observation, 1981	50	80	___	___	___
559	Rock Island Combine, 1981	35	50	___	___	___
560	Rock Island Coach, 1981	35	50	___	___	___
561	Rock Island Coach, 1981	35	50	___	___	___
(9562)	N & W "577" Baggage, 1981	90	125	___	___	___
(9563)	N & W "578" Combine, 1981	90	125	___	___	___
(9564)	N & W "579" Coach, 1981	110	150	___	___	___
(9565)	N & W "580" Coach, 1981	110	150	___	___	___
(9566)	N & W "581" Observation, 81	90	125	___	___	___
(9567)	N & W "582" Vista Dome, 81	425	575	___	___	___
9569	Pennsylvania Combine, 1981	125	150	___	___	___
9570	Pennsylvania Baggage, 1979	125	150	___	___	___
9571	Pennsylvania Pullman, 1979	140	175	___	___	___
9572	Pennsylvania Pullman, 1979	140	175	___	___	___
9573	Pennsylvania Vista Dome, 1979	125	150	___	___	___
9574	Pennsylvania Observation, 1979	125	150	___	___	___
9575	Pennsylvania "Edison", 1979	135	175	___	___	___
9576	Burlington Baggage, 1980	70	100	___	___	___
9577	Burlington Coach, 1980	80	110	___	___	___
9578	Burlington Coach, 1980	80	110	___	___	___
9579	Burlington Vista Dome, 1980	80	110	___	___	___
9580	Burlington Observation, 1980	80	110	___	___	___
9581	Chessie Baggage, 1980	60	80	___	___	___
9582	Chessie Combine, 1980	60	80	___	___	___
9583	Chessie Coach, 1980	60	80	___	___	___
9584	Chessie Coach, 1980	60	80	___	___	___
9585	Chessie Observation, 1980	60	80	___	___	___
9586	Chessie Special Dining Car, 86	110	125	___	___	___
9588	Burlington Vista Dome, 1980	110	150	___	___	___
9589	Southern Pacific Baggage, 1982	100	125	___	___	___

		Exc	LN	Color	Cond	$
9590	Southern Pacific Combine 1982	100	125			
9591	Southern Pacific Pullman, 82-83	100	125			
9592	Southern Pacific Pullman, 82-83	100	125			
9593	S P Observation, 1982-83	100	125			
9594	N Y C Baggage, 1983	100	125			
9595	N Y C Combine, 1983	115	150			
9596	N Y C Pullman, 1983	115	150			
9597	N Y C Pullman, 1983	115	150			
9598	N Y C Observation, 1983	100	125			
9599	Chicago & Alton Dining Car, 86	—	90			
9600	Chessie Hi-cube, 1976	20	25			
9601	Illinois Central Hi-cube, 1976-77	20	25			
9602	A T & S F Hi-cube, 1977	20	25			
9603	Penn Central Hi-cube, 1976-77	20	30			
9604	N & W Hi-cube, 1976-77	20	25			
9605	New Haven Hi-cube, 1976-77	20	30			
9606	Union Pacific Hi-cube, 1976-77	20	25			
9607	Southern Pacific Hi-cube, 76-77	20	25			
9608	Burlington Northern Hi-cube, 77	20	25			
9610	Frisco Hi-cube, 1977	30	50			
9611	T C A Boston Hi-cube, 1978	35	45			
9620	N H L Wales, 1980	15	20			
9621	N H L Campbell, 1980	15	20			
9622	N B A Western, 1980	15	20			
9623	N B A Eastern, 1980	15	20			
9624	National League, 1980	15	20			
9625	American League, 1980	15	20			
9626	A T & S F Hi-cube, 1982-83	15	20			
9627	Union Pacific Hi-cube, 1982-83	15	20			
9628	B N Hi-cube, 1982-83	10	15			
9629	Chessie System Hi-cube, 1983	15	20			
9660	Mickey Mouse Hi-cube, 1977-78	40	50			
9661	Goofy Hi-cube, 1977-78	40	45			
9662	Donald Duck Hi-cube, 1977-78	40	50			
9663	Dumbo Hi-cube, 1978	40	70			
9664	Cinderella Hi-cube, 1978	55	75			
9665	Peter Pan Hi-cube, 1978	40	60			
9666	Pinocchio Hi-cube, 1978	125	200			
9667	Snow White Hi-cube, 1978	350	500			
9668	Pluto Hi-cube, 1978	150	200			
9669	Bambi Hi-cube, 1978	60	100			
9670	Alice In Wonderland Hi-cube, 78	50	75			
9671	Fantasia Hi-cube, 1978	30	40			
9672	Mickey Mouse "50th" Anniversary Hi-cube Boxcar, 1978	395	500			
9678	T T O S Hollywood Hi-cube, 78	25	35			
9700	Southern Boxcar, red, 1972-73	20	25			
9700-1976	(See 9779)					

		Exc	LN	Color	Cond	$
701	B & O Automobile Box., 71-73	20	25			
701	L C C A B & O Boxcar, 1972	100	125			
702	SOO Boxcar, white, 1972-73	20	25			
703	C P Rail Boxcar, red, 1970-71	55	65			
704	N & W Boxcar, brown, 1972	10	25			
705	D & R G W Box., orange, 72-73	12	25			
706	C & O Boxcar, 1972-74	15	20			
706	(See 19706)					
707	M K T Cattle Car, red, 1972-74	15	25			
708	U. S. Mail Boxcar, 1972-75	15	25			
708	Toy Fair, U.S. Mail, 1973	NRS	NRS			
709	State of Maine Boxcar, 1973-74	40	50			
710	Rutland Boxcar, 1973-74	30	40			
711	Southern Boxcar, brown, 1974	20	25			
712	B & O Automobile Box., 73-74	30	40			
713	C P Rail Boxcar, green, 1973-74	20	30			
713	Seasons' Greetings Boxcar, 74	NRS	NRS			
714	D & R G W Boxcar, 1973-74	20	25			
715	C & O Boxcar, 1973-74	20	25			
716	Penn. Central Boxcar, 1973-74	20	30			
717	Union Pacific Boxcar, 1973-74	20	30			
718	C N Boxcar, 1973-74	20	25			
719	New Haven Automobile Boxcar	25	35			
720	Assorted Case of Cars, c. 1974	NRS	NRS			
721	Assorted Case of Cars, c. 1974	NRS	NRS			
723	Toy Fair W P Boxcar, 1974	30	40			
724	Missouri Pacific Boxcar, 1974	35	40			
725	M K T Cattle Car, yellow, 74-75	15	20			
726	Erie-Lack. Boxcar, blue, 1978	25	30			
727	L C C A T A G Boxcar, 1973	200	250			
728	L C C A U P Stockcar, yel., 78	35	45			
729	C P Rail Boxcar, black/white, 79	30	40			
730	C P Rail Box., gray/white, 74-75	25	30			
730	C P Rail Box., gray/black, 74-75	30	35			
731	Milwaukee Road Boxcar, 74-75	15	20			
732	Southern Pacific Boxcar, 1979	30	40			
733	L C C A Airco Box. w/tank, 79	40	55			
734	Bangor & Aroostock Boxcar, 79	25	35			
735	G T W Boxcar, 1974-75	15	20			
737	Central of Vermont Boxcar, 74-75	20	25			
738	Illinois Terminal Boxcar, 1982	50	60			
739	D & R G W Boxcar, yellow, 75	15	20			
739	L C C A R G Boxcar, 1978	NRS	NRS			
740	Chessie Boxcar, yellow, 1974-75	15	20			
742	Seasons Greetings M & St L Boxcar, green, 1975	25	35			
743	Sprite Boxcar, 1974	15	25			
744	Tab Boxcar, 1974	15	25			

		Exc	LN	Color	Cond	$
9745	Fanta Boxcar, 1974	15	25	___	___	___
9747	Chessie System Boxcar, 1975-76	20	25	___	___	___
9748	C P Rail Boxcar, blue, 1975-76	20	30	___	___	___
9749	Penn Central Boxcar, 1975	15	25	___	___	___
9750	D T & I Boxcar, 1975-76	10	20	___	___	___
9751	Frisco Boxcar, 1975-76	15	20	___	___	___
9752	L & N Boxcar, 1975-76	15	20	___	___	___
9753	Maine Central Boxcar, 1975-76	15	25	___	___	___
9754	N Y C Pacemaker Boxcar, 76-77	30	40	___	___	___
9755	Union Pacific Boxcar, 1975-76	20	30	___	___	___
9757	Central of Georgia Boxcar, 1974	20	30	___	___	___
9758	Alaska Boxcar, 1976-77	30	40	___	___	___
9759	Paul Revere Boxcar, 1975-76	40	55	___	___	___
9760	Liberty Bell Boxcar, 1975-76	40	55	___	___	___
9761	George Washington Box., 75-76	40	55	___	___	___
9762	Welcome Toy Fair Boxcar, 75	150	200	___	___	___
9763	Rio Grande Cattle Car, 1976	20	30	___	___	___
9764	G T W Auto Boxcar, 1976-77	20	25	___	___	___
9767	Railbox Boxcar, 1976-77	20	25	___	___	___
9768	B & M Boxcar, 1976-77	15	20	___	___	___
9769	B & L E Boxcar, 1976-77	15	20	___	___	___
9770	N P Boxcar, 1976-77	15	20	___	___	___
9771	N & W Boxcar, 1976-77	20	30	___	___	___
9771	L C C A N & W Box., 1977	NRS	NRS	___	___	___
9772	Great Northern Boxcar, 1975	65	90	___	___	___
9773	N Y C Cattle Car, yellow, 1976	25	35	___	___	___
9774	T C A Southern Belle Boxcar, 75	30	50	___	___	___
9775	M & St L Boxcar, red, 1975	25	35	___	___	___
9776	S P "Overnight" Boxcar, black, 1975	30	50	___	___	___
9777	Virginian Boxcar, 1976-77	15	20	___	___	___
9778	Season's Greetings Boxcar, 75	150	200	___	___	___
9779	T C A Philadelphia Boxcar, 76	35	50	___	___	___
9780	Johnny Cash Boxcar, 1976	35	45	___	___	___
9781	Delaware & Hudson Box., 77-78	20	25	___	___	___
9782	The Rock Boxcar, 1977-78	20	25	___	___	___
9783	B & O "Time Saver" Box., 77-78	30	40	___	___	___
9784	A T & S F Boxcar, red, 1977-78	25	35	___	___	___
9785	Conrail Boxcar, blue, 1977-79	20	25	___	___	___
9786	C & N W Boxcar, brown, 77-79	20	25	___	___	___
9787	Central of N J Boxcar, 1977-79	20	30	___	___	___
9788	Lehigh Valley Boxcar, 1977-79	15	20	___	___	___
9789	Pickens Boxcar, 1977	25	40	___	___	___
9801	B & O Sentinel Box. (Std. O), 75	35	50	___	___	___
9802	Miller High Life Reefer (Std. O), 1975	30	40	___	___	___
9803	Johnson's Wax Box. (Std. O), 75	30	40	___	___	___
9805	Grand Trunk Reefer (Std. O), 75	30	40	___	___	___

		Exc	LN	Color	Cond	$
306	Rock Island Box. (Std. O), 75-76	75	100			
307	Stroh's Beer Reefer (Std. O), 75-76	80	125			
308	U P Box. (Std. O), 1975-76	80	110			
309	Clark Reefer (Std. O), 1975-76	25	40			
311	Pacific Fruit Express Reefer, 1980	25	35			
312	Arm & Hammer Reefer, 1980	15	20			
313	Ruffles Reefer, 1980	10	20			
314	Perrier Reefer, 1980	20	25			
315	N Y C Reefer (Std. O), 1985	70	90			
316	Brachs Reefer, 1980	15	20			
317	Bazooka Gum Reefer, 1980	10	20			
318	Western Maryland Reefer, 1980	25	35			
319	Western Fruit Express Reefer, 81	25	35			
320	Wab. Gon., black (Std. O), 73-74	40	50			
321	S P Gon., tuscan (Std. O), 73-74	40	50			
322	G T W Gon., blue (Std. O), 1974	40	50			
323	A T & S F Flatcar with crates (Standard O), 1976	80	125			
324	N Y C Gon., black (Std. O), 75	60	85			
325	Schaefer Reefer (Std. O), 76-77	55	70			
326	P & L E Boxcar (Std. O), 76-77	80	125			
327	Cutty Sark Reefer, 1984	15	20			
328	J & B Reefer, 1984	15	20			
329	Dewars Reefer, 1984	15	20			
330	Johnny Walker Red Label Reefer, 1984	15	20			
331	Pepsi Cola Reefer, 1982	30	40			
332	Cheerios Reefer, 1982	15	25			
333	Vlasic Pickles Reefer, 1982	15	20			
334	Southern Comfort Reefer, 1983	20	30			
335	Jim Beam Reefer, 1983	20	30			
336	Old Grand-Dad Reefer, 1983	20	30			
337	Wild Turkey Reefer, 1983	20	30			
340	Fleischmann's Gin Reefer, 1985	15	20			
341	Calvert Gin Reefer, 1985	15	20			
342	Seagram's Gin Reefer, 1985	15	20			
343	Tanqueray Gin Reefer, 1985	15	20			
344	Sambuca Reefer, 1986	15	20			
345	Baileys Irish Cream Reefer, 1986	20	25			
346	Seagrams Vodka Reefer, 1986	15	20			
347	Wolfschmidt Vodka Reefer, 86	15	20			
349	Lionel Reefer, orange, 1984	50	70			
350	Budweiser Reefer, 1973-76	20	25			
351	Schlitz Reefer, 1973-76	15	25			
352	Miller Reefer, 1973-76	15	25			
353	Cracker Jack Reefer, caramel, 73	30	35			
353	Cracker Jack Reefer, white, 1974	15	20			
354	Baby Ruth Reefer, 1973-76	15	20			

		Exc	LN	Color	Cond	$
9855	Swift Reefer, 1974-76	20	30			
9856	Old Milwaukee Reefer, 1974-76	15	25			
9858	Butterfinger Reefer, 1973-76	20	25			
9859	Pabst Reefer, 1974-75	15	25			
9860	Gold Medal Reefer, 1973-76	15	20			
9861	Tropicana Reefer, 1976-77	25	30			
9862	Hamm's Reefer, 1975-76	20	25			
9863	R E A Reefer, 1975-76	30	40			
9864	T C A Seattle Reefer, 1974	35	45			
9866	Coors Reefer, 1977	30	40			
9867	Hershey's Reefer, 1976-77	20	40			
9868	T T O S Okl. City Reefer, 1980	40	50			
9869	Santa Fe Reefer, white, 1975	35	50			
9870	Old Dutch Cleanser Reefer, 77-78	15	20			
9871	Carling's Reefer, 1977-78, 1980	20	25			
9872	P F E Reefer, 1977-78	25	35			
9873	Ralston Purina Reefer, 1978	20	30			
9874	Miller Lite Beer Reefer, 1978-79	25	35			
9875	A & P Reefer, 1979	20	25			
9876	Central Vermont Reefer, 1978	30	40			
9877	Gerber's Reefer, 1979-80	30	45			
9878	Good and Plenty Reefer, 1979	15	20			
9879	Hills Bros. Reefer, 1979-80	15	20			
9879	Kraft Reefer, 1979	Not Manufactured				
9880	Santa Fe Reefer (FARR #1), 1979	35	50			
9881	Rath Packing Reefer, 1979	30	40			
9882	N Y R B "Early Bird" Reefer, 79	30	40			
9883	Oreo Reefer, 1979	35	50			
9883	T T O S Phoenix Reefer, 1983	NRS	NRS			
9884	Fritos Reefer, 1981-82	15	20			
9885	Lipton Tea Reefer, 1981-82	15	20			
9886	Mounds Reefer, 1981-82	15	20			
9887	Fruit Growers Reefer, 1984	35	45			
9888	Green Bay & Western Reefer, 83	50	70			
11700	Conrail Limited set, 1987	475	52			
11701	Rail Blazer set, 1987-88	NRS	NRS			
11702	Black Diamond set, 1987	NRS	NRS			
11703	Iron Horse Freight set, 1988-91	125	150			
11704	Southern Freight Runner set, 1987, uncatalogued	—	270			
11705	C S X Unit Train set, 1988	—	530			
11706	Virginia & Truckee Dry Gulch Line set, 1988, uncatalogued	—	240			
11707	Silver Spike set, 1988-89	—	375			
11708	Toys 'R Us Midnight Shift set, 1988, uncatalogued	NRS	NRS			
11708	Midnight Shift set, 1989	NRS	NRS			
11710	C P Rail Freight set, 1989	—	475			

		Exc	LN	Color	Cond	$
11712	Great Lakes Express Service Station set, 1990, uncatalogued	—	275			
11713	S F Dash-8 40B Freight set, 90	—	580			
11714	Badlands Express set, 1990-91	—	CP			
11715	Lionel 90th Anniversary set, 90	—	450			
11716	Lionelville Circus Special set, 1990-91	—	CP			
11716	Lionel Circus Special, 1990-91	—	NRS			
11717	C S X Freight set, 1990	—	250			
11720	Santa Fe Special set, 1991	—	CP			
11721	Mickey's World Tour Train, 91	—	CP			
11722	Girl's Train, 1991	—	CP			
11723	Amtrak Maint. Train set, 1991	—	CP			
11724	Great Northern F-3 A-B-A diesel with RailSounds, 1992	—	CP			
11726	Erie Lackawanna Freight set, 91	—	CP			
11750	McDonald's Nickel Plate Special set, 1987, uncatalogued	NRS	NRS			
11751	49C95171C Sears Pennsylvania Passenger Train set, 1987, uncatalogued	NRS	NRS			
11752	J. C. Penney A C L Timer Master set, 1987, uncatalogued	NRS	NRS			
11756	Hawthorne Freight Flyer set, 1987, uncatalogued	NRS	NRS			
11757	Chrysler Mopar Express set, 1987, uncatlogued	—	300			
11757	Chrysler Mopar Express set, 1988, uncatalogued	—	425			
11758	The Desert King Service Station set, 1989, uncatalogued	—	250			
11759	J. C. Penney Iron Horse set, 1988, uncatalogued	NRS	NRS			
11761	J. C. Penney Iron Horse set, 1988, uncatalogued	NRS	NRS			
11762	True Value Cotter Cannonball set, 1988, uncatalogued	NRS	NRS			
11762	True Value Cotter Cannonball set, 1989, uncatalogued	—	140			
11763	United Model Freight Hauler set, 1988, uncatalogued	NRS	NRS			
11764	49N95178 Sears Iron Horse Freight set, 1988, uncatalogued	—	300			
11765	Shoprite Freight Flyer set, 1988, uncatalogued	—	140			
11770	49GY95280 Sears Circus set, 1989, uncatalogued	—	190			
11771	Kmart Microracers set, 1989, uncatalogued	—	90			

	Exc	LN	Color	Cond	$
11772 Macy's Freight Flyer set, 1989, uncatalogued	—	300			
11773 49GY95281 Sears N Y C Passenger set, 1989, uncatalogued	NRS	NRS			
11774 Ace Hardware Cannonball, 1989, uncatalogued	—	175			
11775 Anheuser-Busch set, 1989, uncat.	—	250			
11776 Pace Iron Works set, 1989, uncatalogued	NRS	NRS			
11777 49N95265 Sears Lionelville Circus set, 1990, uncatalogued	NRS	NRS			
11778 49N95264 Sears Badlands Express set, 1990, uncatalogued	NRS	NRS			
11779 (See 11717)					
11780 49N95266 Sears Northern Pacific Passenger set, 1990, uncatalogued	—	250			
11781 Toys 'R Us Heavy Iron set, 1990, uncatalogued	—	150			
11783 Toys 'R Us Heavy Iron set, 1990, uncatalogued	—	220			
11785 Costco U P Express set, 1990, uncatalogued	—	300			
12700 Erie Magnetic Crane, 1987	175	225			
12701 Operating Fuel Station, 1987	75	90			
12702 Operating Control Tower, 1987	50	65			
12703 Icing Station, 1988-89	75	100			
12704 Dwarf Signal, 1988-91	—	CP			
12705 Lumber Shed, 1988-91	—	CP			
12706 Barrel Loader Building, 87-91	—	CP			
12707 Billboard Set, 1987-91	—	CP			
12708 Street Lamps, 1988-91	—	CP			
12709 Banjo Signal, 1987-91	—	CP			
12710 Engine House, 1987-91	—	CP			
12711 Water Tower, 1987-91	—	CP			
12712 Automatic Ore Loader, 87-88	—	20			
12713 Automatic Gateman, 1987-88	—	35			
12714 Automatic Crossing Gate, 87-91	—	CP			
12715 Illuminated Bumpers, 1987-91	—	CP			
12716 Searchlight Tower, 1987-91	—	CP			
12717 Non-Illum. Bumpers, 1987-91	—	CP			
12718 Barrel Shed, 1987-91	—	CP			
12719 Refreshment Stand, 1988-89	—	75			
12720 Rotary Beacon (Metal), 1988-89	—	40			
12721 Illuminated Extension Bridge, 1989	—	25			
12722 Roadside Diner w/smoke, 88-89	—	40			
12722 Illuminated Extension Bridge with Rock Piers, 1990-91	—	CP			

		Exc	LN	Color	Cond	$
12723	Microwave Tower, 1988-90	—	20			
12724	Signal Bridge, 1988-90	—	40			
12725	Lionel Truck and Trailer, 1989	6	14			
12726	Grain Elevator Kit, 1988-91	—	CP			
12727	Auto. Oper. Semaphore, 89-91	—	CP			
12728	Illuminated Freight Station, 89	—	25			
12729	Mail Pickup Set, 1988-90	—	18			
12730	Plate Girder Bridge, 1988-91	—	CP			
12731	Station Platform, 1988-91	—	CP			
12732	Coal Bag, 1988-91	—	CP			
12733	Watchman's Shanty, 1988-91	—	CP			
12734	Pass./Freight Station, 1989-91	—	CP			
12735	Diesel Horn Shed, 1988-91	—	CP			
12736	Coaling Station, 1988-91	—	CP			
12737	Whistling Freight Shed, 1988-91	—	CP			
12739	Tractor And Tanker, 1989	—	11			
12740	Log Package (3 logs), 1988-91	—	CP			
12741	Intermodal Crane, 1989-90	200	225			
12742	Gooseneck Street Lamps, 89-91	—	CP			
12743	Track Clips (O), 1989	2	4			
12744	Rock Piers, 1989-91	—	CP			
12745	Barrel Pack (6), 1989-91	—	CP			
12746	Operating/Uncoupling Track (O27), 1989-91	—	CP			
12748	Illum. Station Platform, 1989-91	—	CP			
12749	Rotary Radar Antenna, 1989-91	—	CP			
12750	Crane Kit, 1989-91	—	CP			
12751	Shovel Kit, 1989-91	—	CP			
12752	Historical VHS tape, 1989-91	—	CP			
12753	Ore Load to fit ore car, 1989-91	—	CP			
12754	Grad. Trestle Set (22), 1989-91	—	CP			
12755	Elevated Trestle Set (10), 89-91	—	CP			
12756	Lionel Tour: The Making of the Scale Hudson Videotape, 1990-91	—	CP			
12759	Floodlight Tower, 1990-91	—	CP			
12760	Auto. Highway Flasher, 1990-91	—	CP			
12761	Animated Billboard, 1990-91	—	CP			
12762	Freight Station with train control/sounds, 1990-91		Not Manufactured			
12763	Single Signal Bridge, 1990-91	—	CP			
12765	Die-cast Auto Asst., 1990	—	12			
12768	Burning Switch Tower, 1990	—	90			
12770	Arch Under Bridge, 1990-91	—	CP			
12771	Roadside Diner w/smoke, 90-91	—	CP			
12772	Illuminated Ext. Bridge, 90-91	—	CP			
12773	Freight Platform Kit, 1990-91	—	CP			
12774	Lumber Loader Kit, 1990-91	—	CP			
12777	Chevron Tractor & Tank, 90-91	—	CP			

		Exc	LN	Color	Cond	$
12778	Conrail Tractor & Trailer, 1990	—	10			
12779	Lionel Tractor & Grain Rig, 1990	—	10			
12780	RS-1 50-Watt Trans., 1990-91	—	CP			
12781	N & W Intermodal Crane, 90-91	—	CP			
12782	Operating Lift Bridge, 1991	—	CP			
12783	Lionel Tractor with Monon trailer, 1991	—	CP			
12784	Intermodal Containers (3), 1991	—	CP			
12785	Lionel Tractor w/gravel truck, 91	—	CP			
12786	Lionelville Steel Co. Tractor and Trailer, 1991	—	CP			
12790	ZWII Transformer, catalogued in 1991, scheduled for 1992	—	CP			
12791	Animated Passenger Station, 91	—	CP			
12794	L L Die-cast Tractor Unit, 1991	—	CP			
12795	Cable Reels (2), 1991	—	CP			
12797	Crossing Gate and Signal, catalogued in 1991, delayed production until 1992	—	CP			
12798	Forklift Loader Station, 1992	—	CP			
12805	Three Intermodal Containers, 92	—	CP			
12806	Lionel Lumber Truck, 1992	—	CP			
12808	Mobil Tractor and Tanker, 1992	—	CP			
12811	Alka Seltzer Tractor & Trailer, 92	—	CP			
15906	RailSounds Trigger Button, 90-91	—	CP			
16000	P R R Vista Dome, 1987-88	20	25			
16001	P R R Coach, 1987-88	20	25			
16002	P R R Coach, 1987-88	20	25			
16003	P R R Observation, 1987-88	20	25			
16009	Pennsylvania Combine, 1988	—	25			
16010	Dry Gulch Coach, 1988	—	40			
16011	Dry Gulch Coach, 1988	—	40			
16012	Dry Gulch Baggage, 1988	—	40			
16013	Amtrak Lighted Combine, 1988	—	35			
16014	Amtrak Lighted Vista Dome, 88	—	35			
16015	Amtrak Lighted Observation, 88	—	35			
16016	New York Central Baggage, 89	—	25			
16017	New York Central Combine, 89	—	25			
16018	New York Central Coach, 1989	—	25			
16019	New York Central V. D., 1989	—	25			
16020	New York Central Coach, 1989	—	25			
16021	New York Central Obs., 1989	—	25			
16022	Pennsylvania Baggage, 1989	—	22			
16023	Amtrak Coach, 1989	—	23			
16024	Northern Pacific Diner, 1992	—	CP			
16027	Mt. Clemens Combine (S S S) (O27), 1990	—	35			
16028	Detroit Coach (S S S) (O27), 1990	—	35			

		Exc	LN	Color	Cond	$
16029	Lansing Coach (S S S) (O27), 1990	—	35	___	___	___
16030	Chesterfield Observation (S S S) (O27), 1990	—	35	___	___	___
16031	Pennsylvania Dining Car, 1990	—	25	___	___	___
16033	Amtrak Baggage, 1990	—	25	___	___	___
16034	N P Baggage, 1990-91	—	CP	___	___	___
16035	N P Combine, 1990-91	—	CP	___	___	___
16036	N P Coach, 1990-91	—	CP	___	___	___
16037	N P Vista Dome, 1990-91	—	CP	___	___	___
16038	N P Coach, 1990-91	—	CP	___	___	___
16039	N P Observation, 1990-91	—	CP	___	___	___
16040	S P Payroll Car, 1990-91	—	CP	___	___	___
16041	N Y C Dining Car, 1991	—	CP	___	___	___
16042	I C Baggage (O27), 1991	—	CP	___	___	___
16043	I C Combine (O27), 1991	—	CP	___	___	___
16044	I C Coach (O27), 1991	—	CP	___	___	___
16045	I C Vista Dome (O27), 1991	—	CP	___	___	___
16046	I C Coach (O27), 1991	—	CP	___	___	___
16047	I C Observation (O27), 1991	—	CP	___	___	___
16048	Amtrak Diner, 1992	—	CP	___	___	___
16049	Illinois Central Diner, 1992	—	CP	___	___	___
16102	Southern 3-D Tank, 1987	—	35	___	___	___
16103	Lehigh Valley Dome Tank, 1988	15	20	___	___	___
16104	Santa Fe 2-D Tank Car, 1989	—	20	___	___	___
16105	D & R G 3-D Tank Car, 1989	—	40	___	___	___
16106	Mopar Express Tank Car, 1988	—	80	___	___	___
16107	Sunoco 2-D Tank, 1990	—	18	___	___	___
16108	Microracers 1-D Tank, 1989	—	25	___	___	___
16109	B & O 1-D Tank, 1991	—	CP	___	___	___
16110	Sears Circus Oper. Stock Car, 89	—	25	___	___	___
16111	Alaska 1-D Tank, 1990	—	15	___	___	___
16112	Dow 3-D Tank, 1990	—	25			
16113	Diamond Shamrock 2-D Tank Car, 1991	—	CP	___	___	___
16114	Hooker, 1-D Tank, 1991	—	CP	___	___	___
16115	M K T 3-D Tank Car, 1992	—	CP	___	___	___
16116	U.S. Army Tank Car, 1991	—	CP	___	___	___
16200	Rock Island Boxcar, 1987	—	10	___	___	___
16201	Wabash Boxcar, 1988	—	10	___	___	___
16204	Hawthorne Boxcar (Appliance Store)	—	75	___	___	___
(16205)	Mopar Boxcar, 1987-88	—	50	___	___	___
16206	D & R G W Boxcar, 1989	—	60	___	___	___
16207	True Value Boxcar, 1988	—	65	___	___	___
16208	P R R Auto Rack w/cars, 1989	—	35	___	___	___
16209	Disney Magic '88 Sears Set, 88	—	75	___	___	___
16211	Hawthorne Boxcar, 1988	—	70	___	___	___

		Exc	LN	Color	Cond	$
16213	Shop Rite Boxcar, 1988	—	75			
16214	Rio Grande Auto Carrier, 1990	—	31			
16215	Conrail Auto Carrier, 1990	—	31			
16217	B N Auto Carrier w/screens, 92	—	CP			
16219	True Value Boxcar, 1989	—	65			
16220	Ace Hardware Boxcar, 1989	—	45			
16221	Macy's Boxcar, 1989	—	50			
16222	G N Boxcar (O27), 1990	—	12			
16223	Budweiser Billboard Reefer, 89	—	50			
16225	Budweiser Vat Car, 1990	—	70			
16226	Union Pacific Boxcar, 1990	—	30			
16227	Santa Fe Boxcar, 1991	—	CP			
16228	U P Auto Carrier w/screens, 92	—	CP			
16229	Erie Lack. Auto Carrier, 1991	—	CP			
16300	Rock Island Flatcar w/fences, 87	6	8			
16301	L L Barrel Ramp Car, 1987	—	15			
16303	P R R Flatcar w/trailers, 1987	30	40			
16304	Rail Blazer Gondola, 1987	—	10			
16305	Lehigh Valley Ore Car, 1987	40	70			
16306	S F Barrel Ramp Car, 1988	—	15			
16307	Nickel Plate Flatcar w/vans, 88	—	20			
16308	B N Flatcar w/trailer (1), 1989	30	40			
16309	Wabash Gondola, 1988	5	7			
16310	Mopar Express Gondola, 87-88	—	20			
16311	Mopar Express T O F C Flatcar, 1987-88	—	70			
16313	P R R Gondola w/cable reels, 89	5	7			
16314	Wabash Flatcar w/trailers (2), 89	—	20			
16315	P R R Flatcar w/fences, 1989	—	15			
16317	P R R Barrel Ramp Car, 1989	—	16			
16318	L L Flatcar w/wire reels, 1989	—	20			
16320	G N Barrel Ramp Flatcar, 90	—	16			
16321	Sealand T T U X Flatcar with trailer, 1990	—	60			
16322	Sealand T T U X Flat. Set, 1991	—	60	—	—	—
16323	L L Flatcar w/trailers, 1990	—	25			
16324	P R R Flatcar w/cable reels, 90	—	20			
16325	Microracers Barrel Ramp Car, 89	—	21			
16326	S F Flatcar w/cable reels, 1991	—	CP			
16327	Sears Circus Gondola, 1989	—	20			
16328	N P Gondola, 1990	—	8			
16329	Southern Pacific Flatcar with stakes and horses, 1990-91	—	CP	—	—	—
16328	Nickel Plate small Gondola with cable reels, 1990	—	8			
16330	M K T Flat. w/trailers, 1991	—	CP	—	—	—
16331	Southern Railway Barrel Ramp Car, 1990-91			Not Manufactured		

		Exc	LN	Color	Cond	$
6332	Lionel Lines Flatcar w/trans., 91	—	CP			
6333	Frisco Flatcar w/ lumber, 1991	—	CP			
6335	N Y C T O F C Flatcar, 1991	—	CP			
6336	Union Pacific Gondola, 1990	—	20			
16337	C & N W T O F C Flatcar, 91	—	CP			
16338	C & N W T O F C Flatcar, 91	—	CP			
16339	Mickey's World Tour '92 Gondola, 1991	—	CP			
16340	Amtrak Flatcar w/ stakes, 1991		Not Manufactured			
16341	N Y C Transformer Car, 1992	—	CP			
16342	C S X Gon. w/coil covers, 1992	—	CP			
16343	Burlington Gon. w/coil covers,92	—	CP			
16345	S P T. T. U. X., 1992	—	CP			
16348	Liquefied Petroleum Car, 1992	—	CP			
16349	Allis Chalmers Condenser Car, 1992	—	CP			
16350	C P Rail Flatcar, 1991	—	CP			
16352	Cruise Missile Car, 1992	—	CP			
16400	Pennsylvania Two-bay Hop., 89	—	25			
16402	Southern Hopper, 1987	30	40			
16406	C S X Quad w/coal load, 1990	—	30			
16407	Boston & Maine Quad, 1991	—	CP			
16408	Union Pacific Hopper, 1990	—	20			
16500	Rock Island Bobber Cab., 1987	—	25			
16501	L V SP Caboose, 1987	15	20			
16503	N Y C Transfer Cab., 1987	—	12			
16504	Southern N5C Caboose, 1987	—	25			
16505	Wabash Caboose, 1988	8	10			
16506	S F B/W Caboose, 1988	25	30			
(16507)	Mopar Express SP Cab., 87-88	—	50			
16508	L L Microracers SP Cab., 87	—	20			
16509	D & R G W Caboose, 1989	—	30			
16510	New Haven B/W Caboose, 89	—	30			
16511	Penn Bobber Caboose, 1989	5	7			
16513	U P SP type Caboose, 1989	—	22			
16515	L L RailScope SP Cab., 1989	—	25			
16516	L V SP Caboose, 1990	—	24			
16517	A C L B/W Caboose, 1990	—	26			
16518	Chessie B/W Caboose, 1990	—	35			
16519	R I Transfer Caboose, 1990	—	22			
16520	Sears Circus SP Caboose, 1989	—	22			
16521	P R R SP Caboose, 1990	—	12			
16522	Lionelville Circus N5C Caboose, 1990-91	—	CP			
16523	Alaska S/W Caboose, 1990-91	—	CP			
16524	Anheuser-Busch SP Cab., 1989	—	40			
16525	D & H B/W Caboose, 1991	—	CP			
16526	K C Southern Caboose, 1992	—	CP			

		Exc	LN	Color Cond $
16527	W P Cab., 1992	—	CP	
16528	Union Pacific caboose, 1990	—	20	
16529	A T S F SP Caboose, 1991	—	CP	
16530	Mickey's World Tour '92, SP Caboose, 1991	—	CP	
16531	Texas & Pacific Caboose, 1992	—	CP	
16533	C & N B/W Caboose,1992	—	CP	
16535	Erie Lackawanna B/W Cab., 91	—	CP	
16600	I C Coal Dump, 1988	—	20	
16601	C N Searchlight Car, 1988	—	25	
16602	Erie Coal Dump, 1987	—	18	
16603	Detroit Zoo Giraffe Car, 1987	—	25	
16604	N Y Central Log Dump, 1987	—	18	
16605	Bronx Zoo Oper. Giraffe Car, 88	—	28	
16606	Southern Searchlight Car, 87-88	—	20	
16607	Southern Coal Dump, 1987	—	25	
16608	L V Searchlight Car, 1987	30	40	
16609	Lehigh Valley Derrick, 1987	20	25	
16610	Lionel Track Maint. Car, 87-88	—	20	
16611	Santa Fe Log Dump Car, 1988	—	20	
16612	SOO Line Log Dump Car, 1989	—	20	
16613	Katy Coal Dump Car, 1989	—	20	
16614	Reading Cop and Hobo car, 89	—	30	
16615	L L Ext. Searchlight Car, 1989	—	25	
16616	D & R G W Searchlight Car, 89	—	28	
16617	C & N W Boxcar w/E T D, 89	—	25	
16618	S F Track Maintenance Car, 89	—	20	
16619	Wabash Coal Dump Car, 1990	—	20	
16620	C & O Track Maint. Car, 90-91	—	20	
16621	Alaska Log Dump Car, 1990	—	21	
16622	C S X Boxcar w/E T D, 90-91	—	27	
16623	Katy DD Box. w/E T D, 1991	—	CP	
16624	N H Cop & Hobo Boxcar (O27), 1990-91	—	CP	
16625	N Y C Extension Searchlight Car, 1990	—	28	
16626	C S X Searchlight, 1990	—	24	
16627	C S X Log Dump, 1990	—	21	
16628	Lionelville Circus Operating Gondola, 1991	—	CP	
16629	Lionelville Circus Operating Elephant Boxcar, 1990	—	40	
16630	Southern Pacific Operating Cowboy Stock Car, 1990-91	—	CP	
16631	Rock Island Boxcar with steam RailSounds, 1990-91	—	CP	
16632	Burlington Boxcar with diesel RailSounds, 1990	—	140	

		Exc	LN	Color	Cond	$
16633	G N Cop and Hobo Car, 1990-91		Not Manufactured			
16634	W M Coal Dump Car, 1990		Not Manufactured			
16635	C P Track Maint. Car, 1990-91		Not Manufactured			
16636	D & R G Log Dump Car, 91	—	CP			
16637	W P Ext. Searchlight Car, 91	—	CP			
16638	Lionelville Circus Operating Stock Car, 1991	—	CP			
16639	B & O Boxcar, 1991	—	CP			
16640	Rutland Boxcar, 1991	—	CP			
16641	Toys 'R Us Oper. Giraffe Car, 90	—	50			
16642	Goofy 6454-style Boxcar, 1991	—	CP			
16643	Amtrak Coal Dump Car, 1991		Not Manufactured			
16644	Amtrak Crane Car, 1991		Not Manufactured			
16645	Amtrak Work Caboose, 1991		Not Manufactured			
16646	Railroad Boxcar w/E. T. D., 92	—	CP			
16701	Southern Tool Car, 1987	—	45			
16702	Amtrak Bunk Car, 1991		Not Manufactured			
16703	N Y C Tool Car, 1992	—	CP			
16804	Lionel Railroader Club Cab., 91	—	CP			
17000	(See 17107)					
17002	Conrail A C F Hopper, 1987	90	110			
17003	DuPont 2-bay Hopper, 1990	—	80			
17004	M K T A C F 2-bay Hopper, 91	—	CP			
17005	Cargill Center Flow Hopper, 92	—	CP			
17100	Chessie Hopper, 1988	—	50			
17101	Chessie Hopper, 1988	—	50			
17102	Chessie Hopper, 1988	—	50			
17103	Chessie Hopper, 1988	—	50			
17104	Chessie Hopper, 1988	—	50			
17107	Sclair Covered hopper, 1989	—	80			
17108	S F 3-bay Center-flow Hop. 90	—	75			
17109	N & W A C F 3-bay Hop., 91	—	CP			
17110	U P 48-ft. 3-bay (Std. O) Hopper, 1991	—	CP			
17111	Reading 48-ft. 3-bay (Std. O) Hopper, 1991	—	CP			
17112	Erie Lackawanna Hopper, 1992	—	CP			
17200	C P Rail Boxcar, 1989	—	70			
17201	Conrail Boxcar (O), 1987	—	60			
17202	S F Boxcar w/RailSounds, 1990	—	30			
17203	Cotton Belt Boxcar, 1991	—	CP			
17204	Missouri Pacific Boxcar, 1991	—	CP			
17207	Chicago & Illinois and Midland Boxcar, 1992	—	CP			
17208	Union Pacific Boxcar, 1992	—	CP			
17300	Canadian Pacific Reefer (O), 89	—	55			
17301	Conrail Reefer (O), 1987	40	50			
17302	Santa Fe Reefer, 1990	—	75			

		Exc	LN	Color	Cond	$
17400	C P Rail Gon. w/coal load, 89	—	40			
17401	Conrail Gondola (O), 1987	35	50			
17402	S F Gondola w/coal load, 1990	—	45			
17500	C P Rail Flatcar w/logs, 1989	—	55			
17501	Conrail Flatcar (O), 1987	—	40			
17502	S F Flatcar w/trailer, 1990	—	80			
17600	N Y C Caboose, 1987	75	95			
17601	Southern Woodside Caboose, 88	70	85			
17602	Conrail Caboose, 1987	70	85			
17603	Rock Island Caboose, 1988	60	75			
17604	Lackawanna Caboose, 1988	—	60			
17605	Reading Woodside Cab., 1989	—	60			
17606	N Y C Caboose with smoke (Standard O), 1990	—	75			
17607	Reading Caboose with smoke, (Standard O), 1991	—	CP			
17608	Chessie Cab. w/smoke (Std. O), 91	—	CP			
17610	Wabash (Std. O) Caboose, 1991	—	CP			
17611	N Y C Cab. (Std. O), 1990-91	—	CP			
17612	Nickel Plate Road Caboose, 1992	—	CP			
17613	Southern Cab. (Std. O), 1992	—	CP			
17615	N P Cab. (Std. O), 1992	—	CP			
17870	L C C A E C & H Boxcar, 1987	60	75			
(17871)	T T O S Flatcar with Kodak and Xerox Trailer, 1987, "81487"	—	150			
17872	T T O S '88 Anaconda Ore, "81988", 88	—	75			
17873	L C C A Ashland Oil Tank, 1988	40	50			
17874	L O T S '88 M R Log Dump, 1988	—	125			
17875	L O T S P H D Boxcar, "1289", 1989	—	100			
17876	L C C A C N & L Boxcar, 89	60	75			
17877	T T O S M K T Tank Car, 89	—	70			
17880	L C C A D R & G Caboose (L C C A) (Standard O), 1990	65	85			
17882	L O T S B & O Double-door Boxcar with E T D 1990	—	90			
17883	T C A New Georgia Pass., 90	NRS	NRS			
17884	T T O S Columbus & Dayton Boxcar, 1990	—	50			
17885	Artrain 1-D Tank, 1990, uncat.	—	90			
17886	Cyprus Ore Car, 1991	—	CP			
17887/17888	L C C A Conrail Flatcars, 1991	—	CP			
17889	T T O S S P Flatcar, 1991	—	CP			
17890	L O T S C S X Auto Carrier, 91	—	CP			
17900	S F Uni-Body Tank (Std.O), 90	—	60			

No.	Description	Exc	LN	Color	Cond	$
17901	Chevron Uni-Body Tank Car (Standard O), 1990	—	60			
17902	N J Zinc 1-D Tank, 1991	—	CP			
17903	Conoco 1-D Tank, 1991	—	CP			
(18000)	P R R B6 Switcher 0-6-0, 89	—	675			
(18001)	Rock Island Steam 4-8-4, 87	500	650			
(18002)	"785" N Y C Steam 4-6-4, 87	950	1100			
(18003)	Delaware Lack. 4-8-4, 1988	—	650			
(18004)	Reading Pacific 4-6-2, 1989	—	350			
(18005)	Hudson, 1-700E Scale Steam (Standard O), 4-6-4, with RailSounds, 1990	—	1395			
(18006)	Reading 4-8-4, T-1, 1989	—	1000			
(18007)	Southern Pacific, 1991	—	CP			
(18008)	Disneyland 35th Anniv. General Steam 4-4-0, with display case, 1990, "4"	—	335			
(18009)	N Y C Mohawk Steam 4-8-2, 90	—	960			
(18010)	Pennsylvania 6-8-6, S-2, 1991	—	CP			
18011	Chessie Steam Special, 1991	—	CP			
18013	Disneyland 35th Anniversary Engine and Tender without Display Case, 1990	NRS	NRS			
(18014)	Lionel Lines 2-6-4 steam, 1991	—	CP			
18016	N P 4-8-4 Northern & Tdr., 92	—	CP			
18018	Southern 2-8-2 Mikado and Tender, 1992	—	CP			
18100/18101/18102	Santa Fe set, 1991	—	CP			
18103	SF B-unit, 1991	—	CP			
(18200)	Conrail SD-40 Diesel, 1987	250	325			
(18201)	Chessie SD-40, 1988	250	325			
18202	Erie-Lack. SD-40 dum., 1989	—	165			
(18203)	C P Rail SD-40, 1989	—	250			
(18204)	Chessie SD-40 dum., 1990	—	180			
(18205)	Union Pacific GE-8 40C, 1989	—	375			
(18206)	Santa Fe Dash-8 Diesel, 1990	—	375			
18208	B N SD-40 dum. Diesel, 1991	—	CP			
(18300)	Penn. GG-1 Electric, 1987	450	525			
(18301)	Southern F M w/cab., 1988	350	400			
(18302)	G N Electric, 1988	—	250			
(18303)	Amtrak GG-1, 1989	—	425			
18304	Lackawanna, set of multiple unit commuter cars, 1991	—	CP			
18305	Lackawanna, set of multiple unit commuter cars, 1992	—	CP			
(18400)	Santa Fe Snowplow 2-4-2, 87	—	145			
18401	Lionel Handcar, 1987-88	—	50			
18402	Burro Crane, 1988	—	120			
18403	Santa Claus Handcar, 1988	—	40			
(18404)	San Francisco Trolley, 1988	—	120			
18405	S F Operating Burro Crane, 89	—	110			

	Exc	LN	Color Cond $
18406 Lionel Operating Track Maintenance Car, 1989	—	90	___ ___ ___
18407 Snoopy/Woodstock Handcar, 90	—	45	___ ___ ___
18408 Santa Handcar, 1989	—	40	___ ___ ___
18410 Pennsylvania Burro Crane, 1990	—	110	___ ___ ___
18411 C P Fire Fighting Car, 1990	—	90	___ ___ ___
18412 Union Pacific Fire Car, 1990-91		Not Manufactured	
18413 Charlie Brown & Lucy Handcar, 1991	—	CP	___ ___ ___
(18500) Milwaukee Road, GP-9, 1987	175	225	___ ___ ___
(18501) W M NW-2 Switcher, 1989	—	295	___ ___ ___
(18502) L L 90th Anniv. GP-9 1990	—	275	___ ___ ___
(18503) S P NW-2 Switcher with RailSounds, 1990	—	400	___ ___ ___
(18504) Frisco GP-7 Diesel (FF #5), 91	—	245	___ ___ ___
18505 N K P GP-7 Diesel, 1992	—	CP	___ ___ ___
18506 C N Budd Cars, 1992	—	CP	___ ___ ___
18551 (See 18809)			
18552 18813 Engine & Display Case	NRS	NRS	___ ___ ___
18600 Atlantic Coast Line 4-4-2, 1987	—	95	___ ___ ___
(18601) Great Northern 4-4-2, 1988	—	95	___ ___ ___
(18602) P R R Steam 4-4-2, 1987	—	90	___ ___ ___
(18604) Wabash 2-4-2, 1988	—	80	___ ___ ___
(18605) Mopar Express 4-4-2 Columbia, 1987-88	—	60	___ ___ ___
(18606) New York Central 2-6-4, 1989	—	165	___ ___ ___
(18607) Union Pacific 2-6-4, 1989	—	165	___ ___ ___
(18608) D & R G W Steam 2-6-4, 1989	—	150	___ ___ ___
(18609) N P Steam 2-6-4, 1990	—	180	___ ___ ___
(18610) Rock Island Steam 0-4-0, 1990, "8610"	—	190	___ ___ ___
(18611) L L Steam 2-6-4 (S S S), 1990	—	175	___ ___ ___
(18612) C & N W 2-6-4, 1989	—	100	___ ___ ___
18613 N Y C 4-4-2 Columbia, 1989	—	90	___ ___ ___
(18614) Sears Circus Train, 4-4-2 Columbia, 1989	—	75	___ ___ ___
(18615) G T W Steam 4-4-2, "8615", 1990	—	100	___ ___ ___
(18616) N P 4-4-2 Columbia, 1990	—	90	___ ___ ___
18617 Adolphus III, Columbia 4-4-2, 89	—	190	___ ___ ___
(18618) B & O Steam 0-4-4-2, Tender, 1990-91		Not Manufactured	
(18620) I C Steam, 2-6-2, 1991	—	CP	___ ___ ___
18621 Western Pacific Steam 0-4-0, Tender, 1992	—	CP	___ ___ ___
18622 U P 4-4-2, Tender, 1990	—	80	___ ___ ___
18623 Texas & Pacific 4-4-2, Tdr., 92	—	CP	___ ___ ___
(18700) Rock Island Switcher 0-4-0, 87	—	25	___ ___ ___

		Exc	LN	Color	Cond	$
(18702)	V & T R R 4-4-0, 1988	—	140			
(18704)	L L Microracers, 2-4-0, 1989	—	60			
(18705)	Badlands Express (Neptune) Steam 0-4-0, 1990-91	—	CP			
(18706)	A T & S F 2-4-0 Porter, 1991	—	CP			
(18707)	Mickey's World Tour '92, 2-4-0 Porter, 1991	—	CP			
(18716)	Lionelville Circus General Steam 4-4-0, 1990-91	—	CP			
18800	Lehigh Valley GP-9, 1987	100	125			
18801	Santa Fe U36-B, 1987	—	85			
18802	Southern GP-9 Diesel, 1987	—	140			
(18803)	Santa Fe RS-3 Diesel, 1988	—	100			
(18804)	SOO Line RS-3 Diesel, 1988	—	100			
(18805)	Union Pacific RS-3, 1989	—	105			
(18806)	New Haven SD-18, 1989	—	105			
(18807)	L V RS-3 Diesel, 1990	—	110			
(18808)	A C L SD-18 Diesel, 1990	—	110			
(18809)	Susquehanna RS-3, 1989	—	225			
(18810)	C S X SD-18 Diesel, 1990	—	120			
(18811)	Alaska SD-9 Diesel, 1991	—	125			
(18812)	Kansas City Southern GP-33, 91	—	CP			
(18813)	D M & I R SD-18, 1990	—	200			
(18814)	D & H, Alco RS-3, 1991	—	CP			
(18815)	Amtrak, Alco RS-3, 1991		Not Manufactured			
18816	C & N W GP-38-2, 1992	—	CP			
18890	L O T S U P RS-3, 1989	—	125			
(18900)	P R R 0-4-0, "8900" Gas Turbine, 1988-89	—	40			
(1)8901/(1)8902	P R R Alco AA, powered and dummy, 1988	—	125			
(1)8903/(1)8904	Amtrak Alco AA powered and dummy, 1988	—	125			
(1)8906	"8906" EL Alco RS-3, 1991	—	CP			
19000	Blue Comet Dining Car, 1987	—	85			
(1)9001	Southern Crescent Diner, 1987	—	85			
(1)9002	Penn Diner, 1988	—	50			
(1)9003	Milwaukee Road Diner, 1988	—	50			
19010	B & O Dining Car, 1989	—	50			
19015	L L Madison Coach, 1991	—	CP			
19016	L L Madison Coach, 1991	—	CP			
19017	L L Madison Coach, 1991	—	CP			
19018	L L Madison Obs. Car, 1991	—	CP			
19023	Arcata Bay Passenger 1992	—	CP			
19024	Half Moon Bay Passenger, 92	—	CP			
19025	Drakes Bay Passenger, 1992	—	CP			
19026	Sunset Bay Obs., 1992	—	CP			
19100	Amtrak Baggage, "9100", 89	—	150			

		Exc	LN	Color	Cond	$
(19101)	Amtrak Combine, "9101", 1989	—	150			
(19102)	Amtrak Coach, "9102", 1989	—	150			
(19103)	Amtrak V.D., "9103", 1989	—	150			
(19104)	Amtrak Diner, "9104", 1989	—	150			
19105	Amtrak Vista Dome, 1989	—	140			
(19106)	Amtrak Obs., "9106", 1989	—	150			
19107	S P Vista Dome, 1990	—	95			
19108	N & W Vista Dome, 1991	—	CP			
19109	Santa Fe Baggage Car, 1991	—	CP			
19110	Sante Fe Combine, 1991	—	CP			
19111	Santa Fe Dining Car, 1991	—	CP			
19112	Santa Fe Coach, 1991	—	CP			
19113	S F Obs. Car/Vista Dome, 1991	—	CP			
19116	Great Northern Baggage, 1992	—	CP			
19117	Great Northern Combine, 1992	—	CP			
19118	Great Northern Passenger, 1992	—	CP			
19119	Great Northern Vista Dome, 92	—	CP			
19120	Great Northern Obs., 1992	—	CP			
19200	Tidewater Southern Boxcar, 87		18			
19201	Lancaster & Chester Boxcar, 87		90			
19202	Pennsylvania Boxcar, 1987	—	45			
19203	D & T S Boxcar, 1987	—	15			
19204	Milwaukee Road Boxcar, 1987	—	40			
19205	Great Northern Boxcar, 1988	—	40			
19206	Seaboard Boxcar, 1988	—	20			
19207	C P Rail Boxcar, 1988	—	20			
19208	Southern Boxcar, 1988	—	20			
19209	Florida East Coast Boxcar, 1988	—	17			
19210	SOO Line Boxcar, 1989	—	17			
19211	Vermont Railway Boxcar, 1989	—	17			
19212	Pennsylvania Boxcar, 1989	—	20			
19213	S P & S Boxcar, 1989	—	20			
19214	Western Maryland Boxcar, 1989	—	30			
19215	U P Double-door Boxcar, 1990	—	18			
19216	Santa Fe Boxcar, 1990	—	18			
19217	Burlington Boxcar, 1990	—	18			
19218	New Haven Boxcar, 1990	—	18			
19219	L L 1900-1906 Boxcar with RailSounds, 1990	—	120			
19220	L L 1926-1934 Boxcar, 1990	—	25			
19221	L L 1935-1937 Boxcar, 1990	—	25			
19222	L L 1948-1950 Boxcar, 1990	—	25			
19223	L L 1979-1989 Boxcar, 1990	—	25			
19228	Cotton Belt Boxcar, 1991	—	CP			
19229	Frisco Boxcar with RailSounds (FF #5), 1991	—	CP			
19230	Frisco DD Boxcar (FF #5), 1990	—	CP			
19231	T A & G Boxcar, 1991	—	CP			

		Exc	LN	Color	Cond	$
19232	Rock Island DD Boxcar, 1991	—	CP			
19233	Southern Pacific Boxcar, 1991	—	CP			
19234	N Y C Boxcar, 1991	—	CP			
19235	The KATY Boxcar, 1991	—	CP			
19236	Nickel Plate Rd. Boxcar, 1992	—	CP			
19237	Chicago & Illinois and Midland Box., 1992	—	CP			
19238	Kansas City Southern Box., 92	—	CP			
19239	Toronto, Hamilton and Buffalo DD Boxcar, 1992	—	CP			
19240	G N Boxcar, 1992	—	CP			
19241	Mickey Mouse Hi-cube Box., 91	—	CP			
19242	Donald Duck Hi-cube Box., 91	—	CP			
19243	Clinchfield Boxcar, 1991	—	CP			
19300	Pennsylvania Ore Car, 1987	—	22			
19301	Milwaukee Road Ore Car, 1987	—	20			
19302	Milwaukee Road Hopper, 1987	—	30			
19303	Lionel Lines Hopper, 1987	50	70			
19304	G N Covered Hopper, 1988	—	40			
19305	Chessie Ore Car, 1988	—	18			
19307	B & L E Ore Car, 1989	—	17			
19308	Great Northern Ore Car, 1989	—	17			
19309	Seaboard Covered Hopper, 1989	—	20			
19310	L & C Covered Hopper, 1989	—	20			
19311	S P Covered Quad, 1990	—	20			
19312	Reading Quad w/coal load, 1990	—	20			
19313	B & O Ore Car w/load, 1990-91	—	CP			
19315	Amtrak Ore Car w/load, 1991	—	CP			
19316	Wabash Covered Hopper, 91	—	CP			
19317	L V Quad Hopper, part of Girls' Set, 1991	—	CP			
19318	Nickel Plate 4-bay Hopper, 1992	—	CP			
19319	U P 4-bay Hopper, 1992	—	CP			
19324	D & H Reefer, 1991	—	CP			
19400	Milwaukee Road Gondola, 1987	—	30			
19401	Great Northern Gondola, 1988	—	40			
19402	Great Northern Crane Car, 1988	—	50			
19403	W M Gondola w/coal load, 89	—	25			
19404	W M Flatcar w/trailers, 1989	—	30			
19405	Sourthern Operating Crane Car, 6-wheel, 1991	—	CP			
19406	West Point Mint Car, 1991	—	CP			
19408	Frisco Coil Gon. (FF #5), 1991	—	CP			
19409	Southern Flatcar w/stakes, 1991	—	CP			
19410	N Y C Gondola, part of Girls' Set, 1991	—	CP			
19411	N K P Flat. w/Sears trailer, 1992	—	CP			
19412	Frisco 6-whl. Crane Car, 1992	—	CP			

		Exc	LN	Color	Cond	$
19413	Frisco Flatcar w/stakes, 1992	—	CP			
19414	Boston & Maine Gondola, 1991	—	CP			
19500	Milwaukee Road Reefer, 1987	—	35			
19502	C & N W Refrigerator, 1987	—	30			
19503	B & A Refrigerator, 1987	—	35			
19504	N P Refrigerator, 1987	—	30			
19505	G N Refrigerator, 1988	—	45			
19506	Thomas Newcomen Reefer, 88	—	25			
19507	Thomas Edison Reefer, 1988	—	25			
19508	Leonardo Da Vinci Woodside Reefer, 1989	—	20			
19509	Alexander Graham Bell Woodside Reefer, 1989	—	20			
19510	Pennsylvania Stock Car, (FARR #5) 1989	—	30			
19511	Western Maryland Reefer, 1989	—	30			
19512	Wright Brothers Reefer, 1990	—	21			
19513	Ben Franklin Reefer, 1990	—	21			
19515	M R Stock Car, 1990	—	30			
19516	George Washington Reefer, 1989, 1991	—	CP			
19517	Civil War Reefer, 1989, 1991	—	CP			
19518	Man on the Moon Reefer, 1989, 1991	—	CP			
19519	Frisco Stock Car (FF #5), 1991	—	32			
19520	C S X Reefer, 1991	—	CP			
19522	Guglielmo Marconi, 1991	—	CP			
19523	Dr. Robert Goddard, 1991	—	CP			
19525	Speedy Alka Seltzer Reefer, 1991	—	CP			
19526	Jolly Green Giant Reefer, 1991	—	CP			
19527	Nickel Plate Road Reefer, 1992	—	CP			
19528	Joshua L. Cowen Reefer, 1992	—	CP			
19529	A. C. Gilbert Reefer, 1992	—	CP			
19600	Milwaukee Road 1-D Tank, 87	—	35			
19601	North American 1-D Tank, 1989	—	45			
19602	Johnson 1-D Tank Car, 1991	—	35			
19603	GATX 1-Dome Tank Car, 1992	—	CP			
19651	A T & S F Tool Car, 1987	—	25			
19652	Jersey Central Bunk Car, 1988	—	25			
19653	Jersey Central Tool Car, 1988	—	25			
19654	Amtrak Bunk Car, 1989	—	30			
19655	Amtrak Tool Car, 1990-91	—	CP			
19656	M R Bunk Car, w/smoke, 1990	—	60			
19657	Wab. Bunk Car, w/smoke, 1992	—	CP			
19658	N & W Tool Car, 1991	—	CP			
19700	C & O Caboose, 1988	—	60			
19701	M R N5C Caboose, 1987	35	45			
19702	Pennsylvania N5C Caboose, 87	40	50			

		Exc	LN	Color	Cond	$
19703	G N Ext. Vision Caboose, 1988	—	55			
19704	W M Ext. Vis. Caboose, 1989	—	65			
19705	C P Rail Ext. Vis. Caboose, 89	—	45			
19706	U P Ext. Vis. Caboose, 1989	—	65			
19707	S P Searchlight Caboose with smoke, 1990	—	85			
19708	L L 90th Anniv. B/W Cab., 90	—	40			
19709	P R R Work Caboose, 1989	—	80			
19710	Frisco Extended Vision Caboose, with smoke, 1991	—	CP			
19712	Penn. N5C Caboose, 1991	—	CP			
19714	N Y C Searchlight Cab., 1992	—	CP			
19800	Lionelville Cattle Car, 1988	—	100			
19801	Poultry Dispatch Boxcar, 1987	—	35			
19802	Carnation Oper. Milk Car, 1987	—	100			
19803	Reading Ice Car, 1987	—	50			
19804	Wabash Hopper, 1987	—	35			
19805	Santa Fe Boxcar, 1987	—	32			
19806	Pennsylvania Oper. Hopper, 88	—	35			
19807	Penn. Smoking Caboose, 1988	—	65			
19808	N Y C Ice Car, 1988	—	45			
19809	Erie-Lack. Oper. Boxcar, 1988	—	35			
19810	Bosco Milk Car, 1988	—	90			
19811	Monon Oper. Brakeman Car, 90	—	60			
19813	N P Icing Station/Reefer, 1989	—	50			
19815	D & H Brakeman Car, 1992	—	CP			
19879	T C A Valley Forge Diner, 1989	NRS	NRS			
19900	Toy Fair Boxcar, 1987	—	150			
19901	I Love Virginia Boxcar, 1987	—	35			
19902	Toy Fair Boxcar, 1988	—	125			
19903	Christmas Boxcar, 1987	—	30			
19904	Christmas Boxcar, 1988	—	35			
19905	I Love California, 1988	—	20			
19906	I Love Pennsylvania Boxcar, 89	—	20			
19907	Toy Fair Boxcar, 1989	—	120			
19908	Seasons' Greetings Boxcar, 1989	—	25			
19909	I Love New Jersey Boxcar, 1990	—	20			
19910	Season's Greetings Boxcar (O27), 1990	—	25			
19911	1990 Toy Fair Boxcar, 1990	—	120			
19912	"I Love Ohio" Boxcar, 1991	—	CP			
19913	Seasons' Greetings Boxcar, 1991	—	CP			
19914	Toy Fair Boxcar, 1991	—	CP			
19915	"I Love Texas" boxcar, 1992	—	CP			
(33000)	L L RailScope Diesel, 1988	—	275			
33002	L L RailScope w/B &W TV, 88	—	99			
38356	L O T S Dow Chem. Tank, 87	—	50			

		Exc	LN	Color	Cond	$
59629	(See 17874)					
61602	See 1602 from 1986-91					
61606	See 1602 from 1986					
61615	See 1615 from 1986-90					
61615	Cannonball Express, 1989	—	90			
80948	L O T S M C Boxcar, 1985	—	150			
81487	(See 17871)					
81988	(See 17872)					
91687	Freight Flyer set, 1987	—	65			
91687	Freight Flyer set, 1988-90	—	65			
97330	(See 9733)					
121315	L O T S Pennsylvania Boxcar, 1984-90	—	90			
3739469	(See 17877)					
79C95204C	Sears Santa Fe Diesel set, 1971, uncatalogued	NRS	NRS			
79C97101C	Sears Five-unit set, 1971, uncatalogued	NRS	NRS			
79C9715C	Sears Four-unit set, 1975, uncatalogued	NRS	NRS			
79C9717C	Sears Seven-unit set, 1975, uncatalogued	NRS	NRS			
79N9552C	Sears Six-unit set, 1972, uncatalogued	NRS	NRS			
79N9553C	Sears Six-unit Diesel set, 1972, uncatalogued	NRS	NRS			
79N95223C	Sears Six-unit set, 1974, uncatalogued	NRS	NRS			
79N96178C	Sears Four-unit set, 1974, uncatalogued	NRS	NRS			
79N97082C	Sears set, 1970, uncat.	NRS	NRS			
79N97101C	Sears Five-unit set, 1972, uncatalogued	NRS	NRS			
79N98765C	Sears Logging Empire set, 1978, uncatalogued	NRS	NRS			
JC-1	Lionel Johnny Cash Record Album	3	6			
U C S	Remote Control Tracks (O), 1970	5	8			
No Number	Belt Buckle, 1981	15	20			
No Number	Lionel Clock, 1976-77	50	60			
No Number	Lionel Pennant	2	4			
No Number	Lionel Playing Cards, 1975	1	2			
No Number	Wrist watch, 1986	—	120			
No Number	Alton Limited set, 1981	700	800			
No Number	Amtrak set, 1989	—	900			
No Number	B & A Hudson and Standard O Cars set, 1986	2000	2500			
No Number	The Blue Comet set, 1978	525	575			

No Number	Description	Exc	LN	Color	Cond	$
No Number	Chessie Steam Special set, 1980	725	800	___	___	___
No Number	The Coastal Freight set, 91	—	CP	___	___	___
No Number	Favorite Food Freight set, 1981	200	250	___	___	___
No Number	Frisco set, 1991	—	CP	___	___	___
No Number	The General set, 1977	225	275	___	___	___
No Number	Great Northern set, 1981	600	650	___	___	___
No Number	Great Northern set, 1988	420	475	___	___	___
No Number	Illinois Central set, 1985	1200	1400	___	___	___
No Number	Illinois Central set, 1991	—	CP	___	___	___
No Number	Jersey Central set, 1986	475	550	___	___	___
No Number	Joshua Lionel Cowen set, 1980	650	750	___	___	___
No Number	Kmart Special set, 1975, uncatalogued	NRS	NRS	___	___	___
No Number	Lionel Lines set, 1983	700	900	___	___	___
No Number	Madison Cars set, 1991	—	CP	___	___	___
No Number	Mickey Mouse Express set, 1977	1700	2100	___	___	___
No Number	Milwaukee Road set, 1987	—	460	___	___	___
No Number	The Mint Set, 1987	1000	1200	___	___	___
No Number	N Y C set, 1983	1300	1500	___	___	___
No Number	N Y C set, 1989	—	270	___	___	___
No Number	N & W set, 1981	1500	1700	___	___	___
No Number	Northern Pacific set, 1990	—	300	___	___	___
No Number	Pennsylvania set, 1987	—	230	___	___	___
No Number	Pennsylvania set, 1979	1500	1700	___	___	___
No Number	Penn. set (FARR #5), 84	700	800	___	___	___
No Number	Rock Island & Peoria set, 1980	250	325	___	___	___
No Number	Santa Fe set, 1979	600	650	___	___	___
No Number	Santa Fe set, 1991	—	CP	___	___	___
No Number	Southern set, 1983	740	800	___	___	___
No Number	Southern Crescent set, 77	575	675	___	___	___
No Number	S P set, 1982	3200	3700	___	___	___
No Number	The Spirit of '76 set, 1974	650	750	___	___	___
No Number	Texas & Pacific set, 1980	Not Manufactured				
No Number	Texas Zephyr set, 1980	1100	1300	___	___	___
No Number	Toys 'R Us Heavy Iron set, 1984, uncatalogued	NRS	NRS	___	___	___
No Number	Toys 'R Us Midnight Flyer set, 1980, uncatalogued; see 1993					
No Number	Toys 'R Us Thunderball Freight set, 1975, uncatalogued	NRS	NRS	___	___	___
No Number	Union Pacific set, 1980	600	700	___	___	___
No Number	Union Pacific set, 1984	900	1100	___	___	___
No Number	Wabash set, 1986	1100	1250	___	___	___

		Exc	LN	Color	Cond	$
No Number	W M set, 1989	—	440			
No Number	L A S E R Playmat, 1982	—	5			
No Number	Cannonball Playmat	—	5			
No Number	Station Platform, 1983	—	10			
No Number	Rocky Mountain Playmat, 1983	—	3			
No Number	Commando Assault Train Playmat, 1983	—	10			
No Number	Black Cave Playmat, 1982	—	10			
No Number	DOW 3-D Tank, 90-91	NRS	NRS			

O Gauge Classics

44E Locomotive; part of set 51001

350E Locomotive; part of set 51000

350WX Tender; part of set 51000

882 Coach; part of set 51000

883 Coach; part of set 51000

884 Observation; part of set 51000

892 51202 Combination; part of set 51201

893 51203 Coach; part of set 51201

894 51204 Coach; part of set 51201

895 51205 Observation; part of set 51201

1-263E Loco and Tender; part of set 51004

1612 Pullman; part of set 51004

1613 Pullman; part of set 51004

1614 Baggage Car; part of set 51004

1615 Observation; part of set 51004

8124 (See 51300)

8814 51400 Boxcar; part of set 51001

8816 51500 Hopper; part of set 51001

8817 51700 Caboose; part of set 51001

8820 51800 Searchlight Car; part of set 51001

19400 (See 51701)

		Exc	LN	Color	Cond	$
51000	M R Hiawatha set, 1988	—	900			
51001	Lionel #44 Freight Special, 1989	—	725			
51004	Blue Comet set, 1991	—	CP			
51201	Rail Chief Car set, 1990	—	770			
(51202)	"892" Combination; part of set 51201					
(51203)	"893" Coach; part of set 51201					
(51204)	"894" Coach; part of set 51201					
(51205)	"895" Observation; part of set 51201					
51300	Shell Tank Car, 1991	—	CP			
(51400)	"8814" Boxcar; part of set 51001					
51401	Pennsylvania Boxcar, 1991	—	CP			
(51500)	"8816" Hopper; part of set 51001					
51501	B & O Boxcar, 1991	—	CP			
(51700)	"8817" Caboose; part of set 51001					
(51701)	"19400" N Y C Cab., 1991	—	CP			

(51702)	"478039" Penn. Cab., 1991	—	CP	___ ___ ___
(51800)	"8820" Searchlight car; part of set 51001			
478039	(See 51702)			

Standard Gauge Classics

1-318E	Locomotive; part of set 13001
1-381E	(See 13102)
1-384E	(See 13101)
1-390E	(See 13100)
1-400E	(See 13103)
1-408E	(See 13107)
2-390E	13106 Locomotive and Tender; part of set 13002
2-400E	(See 13108)
7E	(See 13104)
183	13413 Parlor/Baggage Car; part of set 13412
184	13414 Parlor Car; part of set 13412
185	13415 Observation; part of set 13412
200	(See 13900)
201	(See 13901)
323	(See 13400)
324	(See 13401)
325	(See 13402)
326	13416 Baggage Car; part of set 13002
327	13417 Parlor Car; part of set 13002
328	13418 Observation; part of set 13002
1217	(See 13702)
1412	13404 Coach; part of set 13403
1412	Coach; part of set 13420
1413	13405 Coach; part of set 13403
1413	Coach; part of set 13420
1414	(See 13407)
1416	13406 Observation; part of set 13403
1416	Observation; part of set 13420
1420	Pullman; part of set 13408
1421	Pullman; part of set 13408
1422	Observation; part of set 13408
1423	(See 13425)
1512	(See 13300)
1513	(See 13600)
1517	(See 13700)
1520	(See 13200)
1989	(See 13602) 1989
1990	(See 13602) 1990
1991	(See 13604) 1991
5130	Flatcar; part of set 13001
5140	Reefer; part of set 13001
5150	Tank Car; part of set 13001
5160	Caboose; part of set 13001

		Exc	LN	Color	Cond	$
13001	Freight Express set, 1990-91	—	CP	___	___	___
13002	Fireball Express set, 1990	—	1100	___	___	___
(13100)	"1-390E" L L Locomotive and Tender, 1988	—	550	___	. ___	___
(13101)	"1-384E"L L Locomotive and Tender, 1989	—	590	___	___	___
(13102)	"1381E" Locomotive, 1989	—	800	___	___	___
(13103)	"1-400E" Blue Comet Steam Locomotive and Tender, 1990	—	1300	___	___	___
(13104)	Old "No. 7E" Locomotive and Tender, 1990	—	800	___	___	___
(13106)	"2-39E" Locomotive and Tender; (see 13002)					
(13107)	"1-408-E" Locomotive, 1991	—	CP	___	___	___
(13108)	"2-400E" Loco and Tender, 91	—	CP	___	___	___
(13200)	"1520" L L Searchlight car, 1989	—	145	___	___	___
(13300)	"1512" L L Gondola, 1989	—	102	___	___	___
13303	200-series Tank Car, 1992	—	CP	___	___	___
(13400)	"323" L L Baggage, 1988	—	200	___	___	___
(13401)	"324" L L Pullman, 1988	—	200	___	___	___
(13402)	"325" L L Obs., 1988	—	200	___	___	___
13403	State Car set, 1989	—	200	___	___	___
(13404)	"1412" Coach; part of set 13403					
(13405)	"1413" Coach; part of set 13403					
(13406)	"1416" Observation; part of set 13403					
(13407)	"1414" Illinois Coach, 1990	—	575	___	___	___
13408	Blue Comet Pass. Car set, 90	NRS	NRS			
13412	Passenger Car set, 1990	—	800	___	___	___
(13413)	"183" Parlor/Baggage Car; part of set 13412					
(13414)	"184" Parlor Car; part of set 13412					
(13415)	"185" Observation; part of set 13412					
(13416)	"326" Baggage Car; part of set 13002					
(13417)	"327" Parlor Car; part of set 13002					
(13418)	"328" Observation; part of set 13002					
13420	State Car set, 1991	—	CP	___	___	___
(13425)	"1423" Blue Comet Passenger Car, 1991	—	CP	___	___	___
(13600)	"1513" Cattle Car, 1989	—	120	___	___	___
13601	(See 13602, 1989)					
(13602)	"13601" Christmas Boxcar, 89	—	100	___	___	___
13602	Season's Greetings Boxcar, 1990	—	170	___	___	___
13604	Season's Greetings Boxcar, 1991	—	CP	___	___	___
13605	200-series Boxcar, 1992	—	CP	___	___	___
(13700)	"1517" Caboose, 1989	—	138	___	___	___
(13702)	"1217" Caboose, 1991	—	CP	___	___	___
(13900)	"200" Trolley, 1989	—	315	___	___	___
(13901)	"201" Trailer, 1989	—	210	___	___	___

Accessories

No.	Description	Exc	LN	Color	Cond	$
13800	Passenger Station 1115, 1988	—	195			
13801	Lionelville Station 126, 1989	—	100			
13802	Runabout Boat, 1990	—	470			
13803	Racing Automobiles, 1991	—	CP			
13804	Tower, 1991	—	CP			
13805	Boat 1-44, 1991	—	CP			
13807	Racing Straight Track, 1991	—	CP			
13808	Racing In. Rad. Curve Trk., 91	—	CP			
13809	Racing Out. Rad. Curve Trk., 91	—	CP			
51900	Signal Bridge and Control Panel, 1989	—	300			

SECTION IV
LARGE SCALE

3   Locomotive; part of set 81007
100   (See 85100)
101   85101 Locomotive; part of set 81000
401   87401 wood-style Gondola; part of set 81000
404   87404 Gondola; part of set 81007
700   (See 87700)
701   87701 wood-style Caboose; part of set 81000
709   87709 Caboose; part of set 81007
2003   (See 85003)
5000   (See 55000 Lionel Lines Locomotive)
5000   (See 85000 Seaboard Systems GP-9)
5001   (See 85001)
5102   (See 85102)
5103   (See 85103)
5104   85104 Locomotive; part of set 81002
5105   85105 Steam Locomotive; part of set 81001
5106   (See 85106)
5107   (See 85107)
5108   (See 85108)
5109   (See 85109)
5110   (See 85110)
5113   85113 Locomotive; part of set 81006
5114   85114 Steam Locomotive; part of set 81004
6000   86000 Passenger Coach; part of set 81001
6001   86001 Passenger Observation; part of set 81001
6002   86002 Passenger Coach; part of set 81006
6003   86003 Passenger Observation; part of set 81006
7400   (See 87400)
7402   (See 87402)
7403   (See 87403)
7405   (See 87405)
7406   (See 87406)
7407   (See 87407)
7500   (See 87500)
7501   (See 87501)
7502   87502 Flatcar; part of set 81002
7503   (See 87503)
7504   (See 87504)
7508   87508 Flatcar; part of set 81004
7702   (See 87702)
7703   (See 87703)
7705   (See 87705)
7706   (See 87706)
7707   (See 87707)

		Exc	LN	Color	Cond	$
7708	(See 87708)					
7704	87704 Caboose; part of set 81002					
7713	(See 87713)					
7716	87716 Caboose; part of set 81004					
7800	(See 87800)					
(55000)	L L RailScope Loco, 1988-89	—	285	___	___	___
81000	Gold Rush Special set, 1987-90	—	80	___	___	___
81001	Thunder Mountain Express set, 1988-89	—	185	___	___	___
81002	Frontier Freight set, 1988-89	—	135	___	___	___
81003	Great Northern set, 1990		Not Manufactured			
81004	North Pole Railroad set, 1989-91	—	CP	___	___	___
81006	Union Pacific Limited set, 90-91	—	CP	___	___	___
81007	Disney Magic Express set, 1990	—	250	___	___	___
81008	Walt Disney World set, 1991		Not Manufactured			
(85000)	"5000" Seaboard Systems GP-9 with RailSounds, 1990	—	340	___	___	___
(85000)	"5000" Seaboard Systems GP-9 with RailSounds, 1991	—	CP	___	___	___
(85001)	"5001" Conrail GP-7 with RailSounds, 1990	—	340	___	___	___
(85001)	"5001" Conrail GP-7 with RailSounds, 1991	—	CP	___	___	___
(85003)	"2003" Burlington Northern GP-20, 1991	—	CP	___	___	___
(85100)	"100" P R R Steam 0-6-0, 87	—	110	___	___	___
85101	"101" Locomotive; part of set 81000					
(85102)	"5102" N Y C Locomotive and Tender, 1988	—	200	___	___	___
(85103)	"5103" A T & S F Locomotive and Tender, 1988	—	225	___	___	___
(85104)	"5104" Locomotive; part of set 81002					
(85105)	"5105" Steam Locomotive; part of set 81001					
(85106)	"5106" Loco and Tender, 1989	—	250	___	___	___
(85107)	"5107" Loco and Tender, 1989	—	250	___	___	___
(85108)	"5108" Locomotive, 1989	—	120	___	___	___
(85109)	"5109" Locomotive, 1989	—	140	___	___	___
(85110)	"5110" Locomotive with RailSounds, 1990	—	65	___	___	___
85111	G N Steam Locomotive, 1990		Not Manufactured			
85112	R I & P Steam Locomotive, 1990		Not Manufactured			
(85113)	"5113" Locomotive; part of set 81006					
(85114)	"5114" Steam Locomotive; part of set 81004					
(86000)	"6000" Passenger Coach; part of set 81001					
(86001)	"6001" Passenger Observation; part of set 81001					
(86002)	"6002" Passenger Coach; part of set 81006					
(86003)	"6003" Passenger Observation; part of set 81006					
87000	N Y C Boxcar, 1989	—	50	___	___	___

		Exc	LN	Color	Cond	$
87001	Pennsylvania Boxcar, 1989	—	45			
87002	A T S F Boxcar, 1988	—	45			
87003	Great Northern Boxcar, 1989	—	45			
87004	Southern Boxcar, 1990	—	46			
87005	N P Boxcar, 1990	—	46			
(87006)	Seasons Greetings Box., 1989	—	70			
87007	Happy Holidays Boxcar, 1990	—	75			
87009	Western Pacific Boxcar, 1991	—	CP			
87100	P F E Reefer, 1988	—	52			
87101	Pennsylvania Reefer, 1988	—	52			
87102	C & O Reefer, 1989	—	50			
87103	Tropicana Reefer, 1990	—	52			
87104	Gerber Reefer, 1990	—	52			
87105	Seaboard Reefer, 1989	—	50			
87107	A & P Reefer, 1991	—	CP			
87200	Lionel Handcar, 1989-90	—	60			
87201	The Milwaukee Road Ore car, 89	—	35			
87202	B & O Ore car, 1989	—	35			
87203	Santa & Snowman Handcar, 90	—	70			
87204	Northern Pacific Ore car, 1990	—	35			
87205	Pennsylvania Ore car, 1990	—	35			
87207	Mickey and Donald Handcar, 91	—	CP			
87400	"7400" P R R Gondola, 1987	—	36			
(87401)	"401" wood-style Gondola; part of set 81000					
(87402)	"7402" A T S F Gondola, 88	—	36			
(87403)	"7403" N Y C Gondola, 1988	—	36			
(87404)	"404" Gondola; part of set 81007					
(87405)	"7405" B & O Gondola, 1989	—	35			
(87406)	"7406" Southern Gondola, 89	—	35			
(87407)	"7407" M-K-T Gondola, 1990	—	35			
(87500)	"7500" D & R G Flatcar, 1988	—	32			
(87501)	"7501" Pennsylvania Flat., 88	—	32			
(87502)	"7502" Flatcar; part of set 81002					
(87503)	"7503" I C Gulf Flatcar, 1989	—	30			
(87504)	"7504" Union Pacific Flat., 89	—	30			
87505	Soo Lines Flatcar, 1990	—	36			
(87508)	"7508" Flatcar; part of set 81004					
87600	Alaska Railroad Tank Car, 1989	—	40			
87601	Santa Fe Tank Car, 1989	—	40			
87602	Gulf Tank Car, 1990	—	43			
87603	Borden Tank Car, 1990	—	43			
87604	Shell Tank Car, 1991	—	CP			
(87700)	"700" Pennsylvania Cab., 87	—	40			
(87701)	"701" wood-style Caboose; part of set 81000					
(87702)	"7702" A T S F Cab., 1988	—	40			
(87703)	"7703" N Y C Caboose, 1988	—	40			
(87704)	"7704" Caboose; part of set 81002					
(87705)	"7705" G N Caboose, 1989	—	50			

		Exc	LN	Color	Cond	$
(87706)	"7706" C & O Caboose, 1989	—	50	___	___	___
(87707)	"7707" B & O Caboose, 1989	—	40	___	___	___
(87708)	"7708" C P Caboose, 1989	—	40	___	___	___
(87709)	"709" Caboose; part of set 81007					
87712	Rock Island & Peoria Caboose, 1990		Not Manufactured			
(87713)	"7713" Pennsylvania Cab., 90	—	50	___	___	___
(87716)	"7716" Caboose; part of set 81004					
(87800)	"7800" N Y C Searchlight Car, 1989-90	—	61	___	___	___
87802	Conrail Boxcar, 1990-91	—	CP	___	___	___
87803	Seaboard Boxcar, 1990-91	—	52	___	___	___
87806	Railway Express Agency Boxcar, 1991		Not Manufactured			

Track and Accessories

		Exc	LN	Color	Cond	$
82000	Straight Trk. 11-3/4" long, 87-91	—	CP	___	___	___
82001	Curved Trk. 13" long, 1987-91	—	CP	___	___	___
82002	Straight Trk. 11-3/4" long, 87-91	—	CP	___	___	___
82003	Curved Track, 13" long, 1987-91	—	CP	___	___	___
82004	Curved Track, wide radius, 15-1/4" long, 1988-91	—	CP	___	___	___
82006	Extra long straight track, 35-1/4" long, 1988-91	—	CP	___	___	___
82007	Remote Switch, RH, 1989-91	—	CP	___	___	___
82008	Remote Switch, LH, 1989-91	—	CP	___	___	___
82101	Lockon with wires, 1988-91	—	CP	___	___	___
82102	Rail Joiners, 6/pkg., 1988-91	—	CP	___	___	___
82103	Couplers, 1 pair, 1988-91	—	CP	___	___	___
82104	Water Tower, 1988-89	—	40	___	___	___
82105	Engine House, 1988-89	—	125	___	___	___
82106	Watchman Shanty, 1988-89	—	50	___	___	___
82107	Passenger/Freight Sta. 1988-89	—	90	___	___	___
82108	Manual Uncoupler, 1988-91	—	CP	___	___	___
82109	Brass Pins, 12/pkg., 1988-91	—	CP	___	___	___
82110	Lumber Shed, 1989	—	35	___	___	___
82111	Freight Platform, 1989	—	75	___	___	___
82112	Figure Set, 6-pc. asst., 1989-91	—	CP	___	___	___
82115	Vehicle Assortment (82116, 82117, 82118), six Fords, 1989	—	45	___	___	___
82115	RailSounds Control, 1991	—	CP	___	___	___
82116	DC Converter Box, 1991	—	CP	___	___	___
82116	Two 1936 Pickups; part of set 82115					
82117	Crossing Gate and Signal, 1991 Production Delayed					
82117	Two 1928 Coupes; part of set 82115					
82118	Two 1936 Station Wagons; part of set 82115					

SECTION V
COLLECTIBLES AND PAPER

		Exc	New	Color	Cond	$
6-1076	Lionel Clock, 1976	250	350			
6-5801	Lighter, 1987	—	4			
6-5802	Lapel Pin, 1987-90	—	4			
6-5803	License Plate, 1987	—	4			
6-5804	Key Chain, 1987	—	5			
6-5805	Ashtray, 1987-90	—	7			
6-5806	Coffee Mug, 1987-90	—	8			
6-5807	Sport Cap, 1987	—	8			
6-5808	Brass Key Chain, 1987-90	—	8			
6-5809	Engineer's Gloves, 1987	—	11			
6-5817	Portable Tool Kit	—	14			
6-5819	Pen and Pencil Set, 1987-90	—	20			
6-5818	Mini Mag Lite, 1987	—	22			
6-5820	Travel Alarm Clock, 1987	—	25			
6-5821	Beverage Coaster Set, 1987	—	80			
6-5822	Quartz Wristwatch, 1987	—	130			
6-5826	Lionel Pennant, 1989-90	—	5			
6-5858	Director's Chair, 1989-90	—	80			
Bill Stern Record 1947						
(A)	Red and white center, black record	40	50			
(B)	Red and purple center, blue record	50	60			
Promo Record 1947(?), 10", with						
	train sounds	NRS	NRS			
Promo Record & Folder 1949, 5-1/2"						
	"Whistles and Bells"	45	55			
Promo Record & Folder 1951-54, 5-1/2"						
	"Lionel Train Sound Effects"	50	60			
Promo Record 1955, "I'm a Lionel						
	(Toot Toot) Engineer"	60	75			
JC-1	Lionel Johnny Cash Album, 1976	NRS	NRS			
No Number	Tin Railroad Pins (5), 1952	130	150			

The following is a partial list of Lionel paper from 1945-1969. For the complete listing, see *Greenberg's Guide to Lionel Paper and Collectibles*. Catalogue measurements are given with width followed by height.

	Good	Exc
1945		
Advance Catalogue	NRS	NRS
Consumer Catalogue 8-1/2" x 11", red & black, 4 pg. folder		
(A) Consumer original	NRS	NRS
(B) Consumer reproduction	—	1
Candid Camera Shots of Lionel Trains 5-7/8" x 8-3/4", 20 pgs.	15	20
Plans and Blue Prints 5-7/8" x 8-13/16", 20 pgs.	15	20
1946		
Advance Catalogue 10-1/2" x 8-5/16", red & black, 24 pgs.	90	150
Consumer Catalogue 8-3/8" x 11-1/4", full-color, 20 pgs.	50	60
Consumer Catalogue Reproduced, 20 pgs.	—	10
Consumer Catalogue Liberty, 8-3/8" x 11-1/4", 16 pgs.	100	140
Instructions for Assembling and Operating Lionel Trains	4	7
Scenic Effects 6" x 9", 24 pgs.	15	20
1947		
Advance Catalogue "The Lionel Line for 1947", 14" x 11",		
22 pgs.	140	175

	Good	Exc
Consumer Catalogue 11-1/4" x 7-5/8", full-color, 32 pgs.	20	40
Instructions for Assembling and Operating Lionel Trains	4	7
Fun With Lionel Model Railroading Red & black, 32 pgs.	5	10
1948		
Advance Catalogue "Lionel for 1948", 14" x 11", 20 pgs.	140	175
Consumer Catalogue 11-1/8" x 8", full-color, 36 pgs.	20	40
Instructions 5-1/2" x 8-1/2", 40 pgs. plus cover	4	7
3D Poster 18" x 19-1/8" w/glasses	20	30
Paper City 38" x 25", six cut-and-assemble buildings	20	30
1949		
Advance Catalogue 17" x 8-1/4", 24 pgs.	140	200
Consumer Catalogue 11-1/4" x 8", full-color, 38 pgs.	90	135
Instructions 5-1/2" x 8-1/2", 56 pgs.	4	7
Track Layouts 11" x 8-1/2", 16 pgs.	10	15
1950		
Advance Catalogue Gold cover, black & white inside pgs.	90	130
Consumer Catalogue 11-1/4" x 8", full-color, 44 pgs.	30	55
Consumer Catalogue 11" x 8", red and black, 40 pgs.	40	70
Instructions 5-1/2" x 8-1/2", 64 pgs.	4	7
Art Prints of 19th Century Locomotives Four color prints	10	15
1951		
Advance Catalogue 11" x 8", red, 24 pgs.	20	40
Consumer Catalogue 11-1/8" x 7-3/4", full-color, 36 pgs.	20	40
Instructions 5-1/2" x 8-1/2", 64 pgs.	4	7
Romance of Model Railroading with Lionel Trains		
9" x 6", 32 pgs.	5	10
1952		
Advance Catalogue 11-1/8" x 8", 40 pgs.	20	40
Consumer Catalogue 11-7/8" x 7-3/4", full-color, 36 pgs.	20	30
Lionel Accessories 9" x 7", 16 pgs.	5	10
Paper City 42" x 22", four vehicles, three buildings	15	25
Offical Book of Rules 4-3/16" x 6-1/8", 16 pgs.	9	15
1953		
Advance Catalogue 11-1/4" x 7-5/8", 44 pgs.	30	50
Consumer Catalogue 11-1/4" x 7-5/8", full-color, 40 pgs.	15	25
Distributor's Advertising Promotions 8-1/2" x 11", 16 pgs.	10	15
How to Operate Lionel Trains 8-1/2" x 5-3/8", 64 pgs.	2	5
Lionel Accessories 9" x 6", red and black, 16 pgs.	5	10
1954		
Advance Catalogue 11-1/4" x 7-5/8", 44 pgs.	20	40
Consumer Catalogue 11-1/4" x 7-5/8", full-color, 44 pgs.	10	20
Distributor's Advertising Promotions 8-3/8" x 11", 16 pgs.	10	15
Accessories Catalogue 9" x 6", 20 pgs.	5	10
How to Operate Lionel Trains 5-1/2" x 8-1/2", 64 pgs.	3	6
1955		
Advance Catalogue 11-1/4" x 7-3/4", b/w, 20 pgs.	10	20
Consumer Catalogue 11-1/4" x 7-5/8", full-color, 44 pgs.	10	20
Elliott Rowland Catalogue 8-3/8" x 11-1/8", pulp paper	10	15
How to Operate Lionel Trains and Accessories 8-1/2" x 5-1/2",		
64 pgs.	2	5
Accessory Catalogue 11-1/4" x 7-3/4", 20 pgs.	7	15
1956		
Advance Catalogue 11" x 8", red cover, 48 pgs.	40	75
Consumer Catalogue 11-1/4" x 7-5/8", full-color, 40 pgs.	7	15
How to Operate Lionel Trains 8-1/2" x 5-1/4", 64 pgs.	2	5
Elliott Rowland Catalogue 8-1/4" x 11", 24 pgs.	5	12

	Good	Ex
1957		
Advance Catalogue 11" x 8-1/4", red & black cover, 56 pgs.	60	9
And Now HO By Lionel 10-7/8" x 7-5/8", 4 pgs.	3	
Consumer Catalogue 11-1/4" x 7-1/2", full-color, 52 pgs.	7	1
Accessory Catalogue 10" x 7-1/2", 32 pgs.	5	1
How to Operate Lionel Trains 8-1/2" x 5-1/2", 64 pgs.	3	
1958		
Advance Catalogue 10-7/8" x 8-1/4", red and black cover, 64 pgs.	10	2
Consumer Catalogue 11-1/4" x 7-5/8", full-color, 56 pgs.	5	1
Accessory Catalogue 11-1/8" x 8", red and black cover, 32 pgs.	3	
HO Catalogue 8-1/4" x 11", full-color, 6 pgs.	3	
1959		
Advance Catalogue 8-1/2" x 10-7/8", full-color cover, 44 pgs.	15	2
Consumer Catalogue 11" x 8-1/2", full-color, 56 pgs.	7	1
Accessory Catalogue 8" x 11", red/black front cover, 36 pgs.	4	
HO Catalogue 8-1/8" x 10-7/8", full-color, 8 pgs.	4	
1960		
Advance Catalogue 8-1/2" x 11", color cover, 60 pgs.	7	1
Consumer Catalogue 11" x 8-3/8", full-color, 56 pgs.	3	
Accessory Catalogue 8-5/8" x 11", 40 pgs.	4	
How to Operate Lionel Trains 8-1/2" x 5-3/8", 64 pgs.	3	
Lionel Track Layout for O27, O and HO Gauges 8-3/8" x 11", 4 pgs.	4	
HO Catalogue 8-1/2" x 10-7/8", full-color, 12 pgs.	4	
How to Operate Lionel HO Trains 8-1/2" x 5-1/2", 24 pgs.	3	
1961		
Advance Catalogue 8-1/2" x 11", color cover, 76 pgs.	15	2
Consumer Catalogue 8-1/2" x 11", red and black cover, 56 pgs.	4	
1962		
Advance Catalogue 8-1/2" x 11", four-color cover, 64 pgs.	10	2
Consumer Catalogue 8-1/2" x 11", 100 pgs.	3	
Accessory Catalogue 8-3/8" x 10-7/8", full-color cover, 62 pgs.	4	
Accessory Catalogue 8-3/8" x 10-7/8", 40 pgs.	4	
1963		
Advance Catalogue 8-1/2" x 11", yellow, b/w cover, 80 pgs.	40	8
Consumer Catalogue 8-3/8" x 10-7/8", pulp paper, 56 pgs.	4	
Accessory Catalogue 8-3/8" x 10-7/8", 40 pgs.	4	
1964		
Consumer Catalogue 8-3/8" x 10-7/8", black and blue ink, 24 pgs.	3	
Lionel Raceways Catalogue 8-1/2" x 11", 12 pgs.	6	1
1965		
Consumer Catalogue 8-1/2" x 10-7/8", 40 pgs.	3	
Lionel-Porter Science Sets 8-1/2" x 11", 12 pgs.	—	3
Lionel-Spear Catalogue 8-1/2" x 11-1/8", 4 pgs.	4	
1966		
Advancd Catalogue 9-7/8" x 8-1/2", color cover, 40 pgs.	100	14
Consumer Catalogue 10-7/8" x 8-3/8", full-color, 40 pgs.	2	
1967		
Catalogue not issued — 1966 catalogue was used.		
1968		
Consumer Catalogue 8-1/2" x 11", full-color, 8 pgs.	3	
1969		
Consumer Catalogue 8-1/2" x 11", full-color, 8 pgs.	2	

RAILROAD NAME ABBREVIATIONS

A C L — Atlantic Coast Line
A L A S K — Alaska Railroad
A T & S F (A T S F) — Atchison, Topeka, and Santa Fe
B A R — Bangor and Aroostook
B C — British Columbia
B & L E — Bessemer and Lake Erie
B & M — Boston and Maine
B N — Burlington Northern
B & O — Baltimore and Ohio
C & A — Chicago and Alton
C B Q — Chicago, Burlington, and Quincy
C N — Canadian National
C & N W (C N W) — Chicago and North Western
C & O — Chesapeake and Ohio
C P — Canadian Pacific
C R I & P — Chicago, Rock Island, and Pacific
C & S — Colorado and Southern
C S X — Chessie System
Detroit & Mack — Detroit and Mackinac
D & H — Delaware and Hudson
D L & W — Delaware, Lackawanna, and Western
D M & I R — Duluth, Missabe, and Iron Range
D & R G — Denver and Rio Grande
D & R G W — Denver and Rio Grande Western
D T & I — Detroit, Toledo, and Ironton
D & T S — Detroit and Toledo Shore Line
E J & E — Elgin, Jolie, and Eastern
E M D — Electro Motive Division
Erie-Lack. — Erie-Lackawanna
F E C — Florida, East Coast
G M & O — Gulf, Mobile, and Ohio
G N — Great Northern
G T W — Grand Trunk Western
I C — Illinois Central
J C — Jersey Central
L & C — Lancaster and Chester
L C C A — Lionel Collectors Club of America
L L — Lionel Lines
L & N — Louisville and Nashville
L N A C — Louisville, New Albany, and Corydon
L O T S — Lionel Operating Train Society
L R C — Lionel Railroaders Club
L V — Lehigh Valley
M C — Michigan Central
M D & W — Minnesota, Dakota, and Western
M K T — Missouri, Kansas, Texas (KATY)
M N S (M N & S) — Minneapolis, Northfield, and Southern
M P (MoPac) — Missouri Pacific
M P A — Maryland and Pennsylvania (Ma and Pa)
M R — Milwaukee Road
M & St L — Missouri and St. Louis

RAILROAD NAME ABBREVIATIONS

N C & St L — Nashville, Chattanooga, and St. Louis
N H — New Haven
N K P — Nickel Plate Road
N P — Northern Pacific
N & W — Norfolk and Western
N Y C — New York Central
N Y N H & H (N Y R B) — New York, New Haven, and Hartford
O N — Ontario Northland
P C — Penn Central
P F E — Pacific Fruit Express
P H D — Port Huron and Detroit
P & L E — Pittsburgh and Lake Erie
P R R — Pennsylvania Railroad
R E A — Railway Express Agency
R F & P — Richmond, Fredericksburg, and Potomac
R G — Rio Grande
R I — Rock Island
R V E — Redwood Valley Express
S C L — Seaboard Coast Line
S F — Santa Fe
S P — Southern Pacific
S P & S — Spokane, Portland, and Seattle
S U N X — Sunoco
T A G — Tennessee, Alabama, and Georgia
T C A — Train Collectors Association
T & P — Texas and Pacific
T P & W — Texas, Peoria, and Western
T T O S — Toy Train Operating Society
T T U X — Trailer Train
U P — Union Pacific
U S M C — United States Marine Corps
Va. Chem. — Virginia Chemical
V & T R R — Virginia and Truckee Railroad
Wab. — Wabash
W & A R R (W & A) — Western and Atlantic Railroad
W M — Western Maryland
W P — Western Pacific